Before You Go

*A Hospice Nurse Shares Her Experiences
Caring for Her Dying Patients*

Linda J. Mancinelli, RN

Blue Heron Books, LLC
Allentown, Pennsylvania

ISBN: 979-8-9871459-4-4
Cover Design by Angie Zumbrano
Blue Heron Book Works, LLC
Allentown, Pennsylvania 18104
www.blueheronbookworks.com
Additional material by Jenna L. Jebitsch, Psy.D
www.goctherapy.com
www.drjennaj.com
Illustrations by Brian P. Yount
www.brianyount.com

I dedicate this book to my mother and grandmother. Thank you for instilling in me the importance of family. I cherish all my memories with you.

"You matter because you are you, and you matter to the end of your life. We (Hospice) will do all we can not only to help you die peacefully, but also to LIVE until you die."

Dame Cecily Saunders, founder of modern hospice, March 8, 2018

Contents

PREFACE

I am a registered nurse who was called to hospice more than thirty years ago. I refer to it as "my calling" because it was always so much more than a job. It has been an experience that has influenced every relationship in my life, both personal and professional. I had the honor of caring for countless patients at the end of their lives. I met and supported their families with the hope that their loved ones would have a "good death." For the most part, I would say this was the outcome. And of course, I did not do this alone. As you read on, you will be introduced to the other professional caregivers. Each one brings a myriad of experience in their particular discipline. Together, with our extraordinary volunteers, we were known as the hospice team.

I would be remiss if I did not mention my earliest interest in becoming a nurse. My maternal grandmother, Maria Gratia Fortunato, lived in our home during the early part of my life. When I was about nine years old, she started to have some difficulty moving around. I'm not sure how it came about, but I recall that I volunteered to help her to wash her feet in a basin in our kitchen. What ordinary young child would have been so eager to perform such a task? Sure, I loved my grandmother. We were quite a team. I watched her cooking with my mother. I remember the wonderful smells that came out of our kitchen. Growing up in an Italian family meant wonderful food and wonderful people sharing their love. How fortunate I am to have had her in my life. I am forever grateful for everything she taught me. But then, I was just a kid, and if there is such a thing as the beginning of a calling, this was it for me. I loved being able to help, to be of real service, and I think that's what motivated me later to become first a nurse and later devote myself to hospice patients.

I decided to author these stories because I wanted each one to be a tribute to the unique individuals I served in their last days. I needed to bring alive all the raw emotions before, during, and after each visit, and especially those in the middle of the night or the wee hours of the morning. Where did I get my strength to leave my warm bed when I got the call? Where did I get my knowledge and outright perseverance to go where I was needed when sleep tried to keep me in that warm bed?

I will tell you—I prayed a lot. I called upon God to be my guide in giving me the answers to the questions that were sure to come from the patients loved ones. I was aware that it was me having these conversations, but it was as if someone else was whispering in my ear guiding my words. Kind of like a divine prompter. I had the power of a greater force assisting me.

I would frequently review what had happened on my drive home. Who was present with the patient? Was the patient at all responsive when I arrived? How severe were the symptoms and was the patient made comfortable before he or she died? In most cases, the death had already taken place. But on some occasions, a routine visit turns into a death visit, as the disease process may have taken a sudden decline. Did the family seem well prepared for this death? Each nurse makes sure she reviews the signs of a pending death with the family. For just as no two people live in the same way, no two people die in the same way. While no amount of preparation can take away the inevitable death, preparation does help the patient's loved ones accept what is happening.

I have often said that being able to attend a person's death was the most honorable thing a nurse could ever do. When we are born, many people attend to us. We are infants so we have no say over who these people are. In the dying process it is quite different. Our hospice patients and their families choose to have us with them. The hospice team begins this journey and at every turn lends the support needed to help the patient be as comfortable as possible. Our goal is also for the family to gain peace. Every visit is well planned. Every team member lends their expertise to form what is called the plan of care. Like a beautiful mosaic or puzzle, everything fits together well. This is the person's own blueprint for the end of their life. Each visit has its own unique quality like the unique piece of that puzzle. As time goes on each puzzle piece is aligned, until there is just one space left. For our hospice patients that space is filled by the last visit. It is the piece filled by the act of their dying.

My Journey to Hospice

People have asked me how I became a hospice nurse. As I said before, I think it was a calling. I started out as a hospital nurse and was in that environment for about 12 years. Because of my personal situation, I needed to have a job that would better suit my childcare needs. I had just become a single mom, and my daughters were nine and five. I searched for a position that would fit my schedule. That is when I found an organization called visiting nurses. I started seeing people in their homes who needed things like dressing changes, diabetic teaching, IV antibiotics, and other specific treatments. These visits were task oriented. I had the opportunity to get to know my patients and their families, especially on visits that involved teaching, as with a new diabetic. I found myself looking forward to these types of visits as I continued to learn more about home care. Little did I know at that time, this would lay the groundwork for the conversations I would have when I transferred into hospice a few years later. The experience I gained during this time was invaluable. Any nurse that decides on a specialty, needs to have a solid foundation in general nursing and medical surgical techniques. This changes when you're seeing a hospice patient. That does not mean they might not have other needs that are more medical. An example of this was George, who you'll read about later. He needed a daily dressing change, but his visits included the emotional component. This physical care was part of the holistic nature of hospice. It demonstrates the idea of treating the whole patient. It also includes conversations with the immediate family and caregivers. With these types of needs, you can see why the workings of the hospice team are so important. No one person can do hospice care alone. Their individual expertise brings the best of everything to each patient and their family.

Having worked so closely with the hospice nurses and social worker at the program where I worked, I began to have an interest in end-of-life care. The supervisor of that team was looking for someone to act as a backup when the hospice nurses were on vacation or had a day off. There were only two of them when the program was first instituted. I said that was something I was interested in and asked if I could shadow the hospice nurses to really get a feel for what a typical visit might look like. They readily obliged. To see them interacting with these patients and their families gave me a sense of what end of life care should be. I learned about which diagnoses were the most common primary ones for the hospice patients currently on service. At that time, most patients had some type of cancer. I was greatly enthused and asked many questions during our ride between patients. With every visit my interest in being a hospice nurse became clearer. I could see myself doing this for a long time. Little did I know that time would end up being over 30 years.

After people realize how and why I entered the hospice field, the next question often is, "Isn't this depressing work? How do you do this day after day, knowing that every person you see will die?" Here's what I'd like to share with everyone. The knowledge that I am helping someone and their families at such a difficult time in their life is an overwhelming honor. I am a witness to so many last events. Things like the last Christmas a person will spend with their family, the last wedding anniversary they will celebrate with their spouse. I have seen the power of the human spirit willing itself to hang on for these final occasions. I have seen people at the end of their life, waiting for the birth of that grandchild. Would you say it was a miracle that they died the day after? There have been countless times when a person will wait until a relative who is traveling many miles to see them finally arrives at their bedside. The most remarkable event I was able to facilitate and share in involved a woman who had given birth to a baby as a teenager but had never seen the child. She had kept up with his whereabouts through the years and had known what he was up to, though she had never confided in her husband about him. With assistance from the social worker and a local attorney, she was able to speak with him before she died, and she told her husband about what had happened. He was extremely supportive and understanding. He even offered to stay connected with the young man if it was agreeable to him, which it was. The knowledge that the situation had been remedied brought great peace to this patient before she died. The fact that she had shared this with her husband brought great peace to him as well.

This is just one example of an event that as a hospice nurse I've had the privilege to be part of. I call things like this "little miracles." How could this be depressing to me? How could this be sad? Yes, the actual time of death is sad. But I also take great solace in knowing that I had some part in helping my patients and their family to be ready for their journey. My hope is that when the day comes for me to leave this earth, as I reach the end of my own journey, I might see people I recognize. And perhaps they will recognize me. This will be a joyous day.

SHARING MY STORIES

GEORGE

George was a retired attorney who lived in an assisted living facility. I saw him daily to do wound care on his back. Most mornings the hospice aide or I would be the one to awaken George. I could tell from the first day I met him that he was a professional man. He greeted me with a formal, "Good morning, Linda." This was my signal to begin his treatment, no time wasted on idle conversation. That would come later. It was part of my role as a hospice nurse to have meaningful conversation with my patients, but only if they would allow it. I would often answer questions and try to relate to any fears they might be expressing. I found this difficult to do with George. It would take three or four visits before he felt comfortable talking with me on a more personal level. The health aide met me in his room. She would assist in turning him, which made caring for his wounds much easier. She then would help him get bathed and dressed. We worked together to transfer him into his wheelchair so that he could be taken to the dining room for breakfast.

This is how we began. Every day for over a month, the aide and George and I became a three-person team. We worked like a well-oiled machine. When giving him care, he agreed to trust us. I would say he even looked forward to our visits. He commented once that he missed this on the weekends when different staff filled in.

It must have felt strange to George not to be wearing a suit and tie, which was his usual attire as an attorney. The fact that he could usually be found wearing sweats or pajamas was quite a change for this proper gentleman. One day I had to speak with him in the dining room about a change needed in our schedule. I observed some of his table mates being less than proper in their table manners. He told me the next day about how upset this made him. We allowed him to vent, and we finally chalked it up to their being unaware of how to conduct themselves in company. The lunches he remembered as a professional were certainly nothing like this.

As we got to know him, George's demeanor softened. He would tell the stories of the war and how his service had affected him. As we spoke, I thought of my own father, also a World War II Army veteran. The stories were short, without the detail one might expect to hear, and I couldn't help but think that it was too painful to recall this time in his life. It may have been difficult for him to recall those fighting with him who did not make it home. It was clear George was guarded in what he was willing to share. My dad never spoke of the war with me or either of my two brothers, but then again, we never asked him about it. It wasn't until he had grandchildren that we learned of his great service. It seemed this younger generation was more comfortable urging their grandfather to speak of these things. My brothers and I did not feel as comfortable as our children did in asking difficult questions. It made me sad to think there was so much I could have learned about my father on this subject. I would have to rely on the memories of my children to fill in those gaps.

We also learned about George's family. That is, whatever he was willing to share. He had one child, a daughter named Rebecca. I spoke with her at least weekly. She lived about two hours away and was his only child. From what I could gather, she had a very demanding job that required long hours. She had shared with me that she wished she had more time to visit her father. Her concern, however, could not be denied. He accepted the situation and spoke of her with great pride and no hint of judgment regarding her limited visits to him.

Ask for George's wife, they were college sweethearts. He spoke of her with great pride, love, and admiration. Margaret worked as a legal secretary, so they had their work interests in common, but I don't believe they ever worked together. There were no personal photographs in his room. I never asked why. I thought this was not something George needed to keep her memory alive. Remembering her and her thoughts was enough for him.

I made it a point to call Rebecca whenever there was a change in her father's condition. Having been in a similar situation when my own mother was on hospice care, I closely identified with this woman who was going through such a hard time in her life. I learned she was divorced and had no children. Like her, I did not live close to my parent, so I depended on reports from her hospice nurse for updates on her condition. What is ironic is that I was attending the death of one of my hospice patients when I received a call from my mother's nurse that her condition had drastically changed. I drove the thirty miles to the nursing home where she resided. Many thoughts crossed my mind as I made that trip. I had to remind myself of the phrase I had spoken to many family members whose loved ones I had cared for. "Some people wait for someone to come, and some people wait for someone to go." I would offer this explanation when someone was distraught about not being present when their loved one died.

My mother chose not to wait for me. I accepted that. Women who were mothers were very protective of their children to the point that they did not want to die in their presence. I know that is what was in my mother's heart as she left us. I believe that it's a type of love you don't see in any other situation.

Rebecca shared with me that in one of her conversations with her father, he told her he was receiving excellent care. He told her how pleased he was with the hospice team and the staff at the assisted living. I'm sure that must have eased her mind and reassured me that our team was working well with the facility staff.

Not every family member is the same. Not all of them need the same attention or the same amount of contact from me. As the nurse, you need to evaluate their needs. After that, you proceed to make sure that when the phone call is completed, they are at peace and know that their loved one is receiving the best care possible.

I felt that way after every conversation with George's daughter. I had explained to her at our initial visit, as we did with all families, that the family is a unit of care. We are not just caring for the person who is ill. We are deeply concerned about the family and caregivers as well. And that is the way it was with every case and with every new family I would meet. I approached them as if this was the first time I was meeting a hospice family even though I had repeated these facts numerous times before to other families. My goal was always to give them the best care.

As George became weaker, I knew that his death would be coming in the next few days. And so, it did. I was not present at George's death. He died during the night. I received the message via our daily phone report. Since he lived in assisted living, one of the staff members called the information into our on-call nurse. I was told that he was not alone. Someone from the facility was with him. That eased my mind and made my heart a little lighter. Although it may happen on occasion, no one should die alone. The staff who attended his death said he was comfortable and had no discernible pain or untoward symptoms. This was the best news I could have received as his hospice nurse.

Our chaplain reached out to the administrator at the facility where George lived. She agreed that the celebration of his life would be a wonderful gesture. This was something we always offered to facilities. I composed a poem about George which I recited at the service and sent a copy to George's daughter. Prayers were offered. Residents were invited to give remarks about George. I offered a few words thanking him for allowing our team to care for him. I expressed gratitude at collaborating with the staff to make his last days as comfortable as possible. Everyone agreed it was a valuable experience.

What did I learn from George? He showed me the difficulty that a professional person can have when he must relinquish control to another professional, usually a person he does not know. He must allow this virtual stranger into his life and learn to trust him or her. When this occurs, a special bond begins to form that will last until that person's death. At least it was like that with George and me. From the many stories he shared about his lengthy career as an attorney, it was clear he was a perfectionist and he expected no less from me. I strove to do that for George every day. This is the lesson he taught me: each person under your care is an individual and deserves to be treated as such. It is incumbent upon you as a professional to administer to each of your patients in a manner that affords them the best possible care for them. I know this is how George conducted himself in his law practice. For me, it has always been a matter of professional pride.

I still talk with George. I can still hear him saying as I would finish his care, "Good job, Linda." I considered that high praise coming from him. My memories of George lift me up on days when I need a little encouragement and when people aren't so forthcoming with their appreciation. I know they feel it and that's enough. This is the gift he gave to me, and I will always thank him for it.

The Man in 416

I would start each day at 8:00 AM in the room on the second
floor
To render care and tend his wounds, I knocked upon the door
I would call his name and he would say
Come in and how are you?
And so began a special time between this unlikely two

He spoke of sports and family and stories of the war
And even songs of battle, sung so many times before
Though illness claimed his body, his mind remained alert
And seldom did he utter a word about the growing hurt

We knew that time was passing as his limbs grew tired and weak
And that the end would come too soon
But of this we dare not speak
And so, it did, and I would weep with others who gave him care
It would be strange to start my day and not to see him there

He taught me about a quiet strength, the strongest kind of all
Throughout his life's adversities, with this he could not fall
For I will always reminisce about the joy I'd seen
Caring for my special friend, the man in 416

JOSHUA

This case was particularly difficult as I was caring for a dying child. Joshua was diagnosed with a cancerous brain tumor in October of his thirteenth year. My visits began with a greeting from Josh's dog, Sunny. She would race down the steps as soon as I opened the door. She was a collie mixed breed. I patted her on the head and promised her a treat if she behaved during the visit. Like other visiting nurses, I kept a supply of dog biscuits in the outside pocket of my nursing bag. When I turned in that direction, she knew it was time for her to be rewarded. It was a little dance she and I did. Josh would observe from his recliner and laugh because he knew what was coming. She was his constant companion until the very end. He had only had her for about a year. The bond they shared was undeniable.

"I believe Sunny might be your best friend," I would say to Josh.

He gave me a sheepish grin, and his green eyes lit up with delight. They had a way of speaking to you and would change with Josh's mood. When he had a rough night, his gaze was more serious, and he would stare into the room. When his pain was well controlled and he was having a good day, his eyes were bright and well-focused. Gazing up at me with his red hair framing his face, I could almost forget he was dying.

Continuing with his assessment brought me back to reality. It was time to ask about his pain.

"What is your number today, Josh?" I would inquire.

"Oh, about a six or seven," he would answer.

Our patients are taught to rate their pain using a numeric scale. The number would be from one, for no or little pain, up to 10 for the worst pain a person ever experienced. He agreed he would be more comfortable with a three or four. This indicated to me that we needed to look at a change in the dose of his pain medication. At this point I invited his mother into the room to go over my recommendations. Mother and patient agreed, so I placed the call to the physician for the order. Joshua seemed pleased, as did Mom. It made me think of all the skinned knees and splinters, coughs and fevers, I had dealt with for my own two daughters. Josh's discomfort was miles from this, but somehow, I still knew how his mother felt. We moms want to take away all our children's pain. We want to fix everything and make it right. Our hearts break when we know that may not always be the result. I reassured Joshua's mom that this new dose of pain medication would make him much more comfortable. I would call in the morning to see how their night had gone. If more changes were indicated, they could be made as well. As we tell all our families, "Your hospice nurses are only a phone call away." She nodded in agreement and gave a soft smile. I smiled too, feeling that I may have eased her mind. For me, this was a successful outcome.

Josh lived with his parents and his older brother James in a modest home. James was usually at work during my visits, but I did speak to him on the phone. I tried to give him answers that would put his mind at ease. Sometimes that was not possible, but I did give him the opportunity to ask any questions. Our social worker, whose hours were more flexible, met with him in the evening and on certain Saturdays. Having a younger brother, myself, I wondered how I would feel if he was on hospice care. Would I question why I wasn't the one dying since I was the older sibling? Would I be mad at God? Even though, there were times when I considered him a pest, I could not imagine my life without him. I shared this thought with James.

He laughed at this remark and acknowledged, "Yeah, that's the way it is with me and Josh."

This is how siblings react. I know I'd be heartbroken if my younger brother was terminally ill, and yes, I would be angry. Growing up in my family, we were always taught to protect each other. How would it feel if this person I so loved suddenly was not in my life anymore? I shared these feelings with James. I wanted to know if he was having similar feelings. I wanted him to know he was not alone. I could see him becoming emotional as tears swelled in his eyes. I asked him if he cried about his brother's illness. He shared that he did not like to show that kind of emotion in the house, because he didn't want to upset Joshua or their mother. I offered a listening ear anytime he wanted to talk. I explained how the hospice team was there to support him, whatever that might mean to him personally. I have shared with many people the importance and value of sitting in silence as well. Sometimes all people need is to know that you are there in case they are ready to talk. And if not, the fact that you accept the silence is really a gift. James acknowledged that he was glad we had spoken.

"I'm glad my mom decided to call hospice," he told me, "I'm glad there are people like you here to help us."

I nodded in agreement as I touched his arm. He said he would call me if he needed to. It was a worthwhile conversation.

On one of my visits, I sat with Josh's mom as we shared a cup of coffee at her kitchen table. It's been my experience that this is the best place for a real conversation. Here I am, a hospice nurse, facing the certain death of every patient I care for. But sitting here with a mother, whose child would die in a matter of days or weeks, was very different. As a mother myself, I could not emotionally comprehend how her life could possibly go on. I wondered, how was she really coping? How would I cope in a similar situation? These difficult questions to which I really had no answers haunted me.

She acknowledged that it was difficult. She said she found great strength in her faith. Her pastor has visited throughout Josh's illness to support her and pray for her and the family. This pastor had baptized Josh many years ago, and he was familiar with the family and all the details of Josh's illness. He was a great comfort to everyone involved in Josh's care. Our hospice chaplain also served as a spiritual support. He contacted their pastor, and they shared information about this wonderful young boy. They discussed how together they could best help this family. Mom knew she had the support of her husband and older son as well, and that was very comforting to her. She described Joshua as a gift from God. She had learned so much from him in his short life. Now it was time to let him go back to his heavenly home. I admire this woman who found a way to release her son.

I knew from experience that respiratory issues may be occurring with Joshua. I ordered an oxygen concentrator to be brought into the home. It was not something he would have to use continuously, but it would be available when Josh's breathing became labored. There is nothing that makes a loved one feel more helpless than watching someone fighting for breath. These changes seem to be a constant reminder of how sick he really was. Everything about Josh had changed since he became ill. I will never forget a picture of him in his baseball uniform, which hung on the living room wall. I had to look very closely to recognize the boy in the photo with the boy in front of me. His facial features now revealed what is known as moonface. This is a swelling of the face and around the eyes. It is a common side effect in people who are on steroids which are used to control swelling. His mother shared that this was probably one of the saddest things for her to witness. The fact that he could no longer play baseball broke his heart. He was a good player and missed the games as well as the camaraderie of his friends.

"I was a pitcher," he said, "And sometimes I played third base. I guess I was pretty good."

We all had a little chuckle about that because Josh was

very good. This memory brought back a sadness in his mother's face. With each new symptom, Josh's demeanor changed. For things like pain, nausea, and shortness of breath there were always new interventions to try. But there was nothing I could do to shrink the tumor that was taking over his body. It is a very emotional place to be, when you feel, as a nurse, you have reached an impasse.

I shared this case with one of our social workers, as well as other disciplines on the hospice team. Along with James, she lent great support to Joshua and his mother and father. It was obvious that his father held the role of head of the household. I would describe him as a quiet, hardworking man. He talked about long hours at his job that kept him from coming home as early as he would have liked, especially now that Josh was so ill. He was not quick to show emotion. Clearly, he loved his family. Clearly, he was distraught about the impending death of his youngest child.

"Do you have any close friends or someone you can talk to?" I asked.

"Well, Pastor has been stopping by. Sometimes we take a walk in the back woods so we can talk in private. I wouldn't want my wife or kids to see that I was upset about Josh. I mean, they know I am, but I'm just trying to be strong for everyone."

I told him I admired him. I was glad that he and the pastor had made that connection. The philosophy of hospice care says the family is a unit of care. And this includes any animals or pets. I offered the services of one of our volunteers to help with Sunny. They readily offered to take her for walks and give her the extra attention she may have been missing. With the family being so busy with Josh's care, time spent with Sunny had been drastically reduced. As funny as this might sound, animals have a change in personality when their masters become ill. Sunny seemed to know it was not a good idea to be jumping on Josh's lap. She knew her place. She was curled up at Josh's feet near the recliner. And she was glad to stay there.

As with most patients with brain tumors, Josh's course of treatment was grueling, to say the least. He was in a hospital in Philadelphia for six weeks of chemotherapy and radiation. His mother shared with me incredible stories about gifts he had received from the organization Dream Come True. This is a group dedicated to fulfilling the wishes of seriously and terminally ill children. His favorite gift was a personal computer. It kept him busy on days when his pain may have been more acute. This and other symptoms seemed to be a constant reminder of how ill he truly was. Joshua agreed to try to teach me the basics about using his new computer. I would have to say this offered much comedy relief in a serious situation. He was an extremely patient teacher as I was not the best student. Let's say I was willing but did not have much prior knowledge of things technical. He taught me a few simple games which he allowed me to win at times. All in all, it was a lot of fun and a nice break from my clinical duties. I have several pictures of Joshua and me at the computer. It was a break from my clinical duties. I consider them among my fondest memories of this special boy.

His family did everything in their power to help Joshua to be a normal kid. His mother reached out to his closest friends to ask if they'd be willing to visit Josh. Three of them responded. She acknowledged that it may be difficult for these young boys to see Josh looking so different now. Most of them had probably never known a young person with cancer. Seeing someone their own age looking so ill had the potential to be very scary. I suggested that she ask his friends to call him on the phone instead. She would know which days he felt strong enough to speak with them. This connection could be especially important to him. Knowing that his friends still thought about him, even though they were not able to visit, might help lift his spirits.

The physical therapists also played a vital part in Josh's care. He tried to keep Josh as mobile as possible with a gentle range of motion exercises. He also taught his mother this regime. It was important to encourage Josh to do whatever he could, until he could no longer be active. We planned a trip to the seashore. Josh had never seen the ocean or beach. The therapist made plans to have a special type of wheelchair available for use on the beach. The social worker made the necessary calls to facilitate the trip. Everyone was extremely excited! Our part of the next few visits was set aside to talk about "the trip." What would the day be like? What would we be eating? Would we be able to get Josh close enough to the shoreline for him to feel the ocean? This would be another dream come true for Josh. We were so happy to be a part of it. Unfortunately, he died three days prior to the day we were to leave. Part of mourning his death was mourning the fact that the dream of this trip would not be fulfilled. We supported each other in the knowledge that we did all we could to try and get Josh to a place he had never been. I mention this to illustrate the lengths the members of the hospice team will go to in fulfilling their patients last wishes.

I was on call the night Joshua died. I believe it was divine intervention that I would be the nurse making that last visit. His mother called me late at night. I knew instantly that for her to be calling, something was seriously wrong. She shared that Josh's condition had taken a turn for the worse. I coaxed myself from under the warm covers. I prayed as I usually did on these types of calls. "Dear God, give me the words to comfort this family. Let this be a peaceful transition for Josh. Give his parents the strength they need at this most challenging time." I drove to the house on these now familiar roads. But somehow this trip was different. There was a sense of urgency that I get there as soon as I could. It had started to snow. I knew the roads would be getting more slippery as each minute passed. I needed to be safe and alert. The drive took about 35 minutes. I knew what was waiting for me at the end of my journey. I would be saying goodbye to Joshua.

As I entered the house, I could sense there was a change. Sunny did not greet me, rather she lay still next to Josh's side. He was sitting in the recliner chair, which had been his most comfortable place of rest. His breathing was starting to become labored and irregular. In medical terms, this is referred to as Cheyne-Stokes breathing. It is a distinctive pattern of shallow breathing paired with no breathing at all. It is an exceedingly awkward thing to watch if you are a family member or caregiver. I had discussed with his mother what medications to give and what dose to help relieve this discomfort. These doses were discussed with the ordering physician. Families are taught to administer comfort medications as part of the teaching for home hospice care. They also know they can call the hospice office anytime during the day or after hours. An on-call nurse is always available to answer questions or concerns. Unscheduled visits can also be made if indicated. I instructed her to give additional liquid morphine at this time as well as another medication called Lorazepam. This is also known as Ativan. Again, these changes were made under the direction of Joshua's physician. This would help him to relax and in turn relax his breathing as well.

We all felt so helpless as we watched him struggle to say something. The few words we could discern were "I have to. I have to." He repeated this phrase several times. Try as we might, we were not successful at figuring out what he needed to do or what we needed to do for him. We were able to bring comfort to Joshua eventually with the proper dosing of morphine and Ativan. A large part of end-of-life care is knowing when to start medications the doctor has ordered and knowing when to ask for an increase. I called the attending physician several times during the night for these orders.

After praying for divine intervention and the proper titrating (increasing) of medications, we were finally able to bring comfort to our little fighter. I had called the social worker and physical therapist who had been such an integral part of Joshua's care. They arrived within an hour or so. Both were a great comfort to the family and me. We sat around Joshua's recliner and started to recount stories of our visits with him. What a strong young man he was. He never complained to any of us. He loved his dog, Sunny, his best friend. How we were all going to miss him so much. How much he meant to us.

I am pleased to say he died peacefully, with his family surrounding him and of course his faithful dog, Sunny, at his side. Animals often show a definite change in their demeanor when they are present at the death of their masters. I have witnessed this scenario with other patients who had animals. Sunny became very attentive. She got as close to Josh's recliner as she could. It was almost as if I could hear her crying. She would certainly miss her young master whose protector she had been for the past year or so. The profound connection between pets and people is astounding, a true lesson of unconditional love. The way they communicate is incredibly special. The bond is undeniable. And so, it was with these two.

About 3 days after Joshua's death, I received a call from his mother. She said he came to her in a dream. Joshua wanted to tell her what he was trying to say that morning he died. He was trying to tell her that it was time for him to leave. He was trying to say "I have to go. I have to go." This was his final gift to his mother. I believe he was trying to prepare her for the fact that he was now leaving her. She somehow took great solace in this message from him. I must admit, so did I.

This account of Joshua's death and the part played by our team illustrates so well the difference hospice can make in the care of a dying person at home. You know you have helped ease someone's pain and suffering. The hope is that this brings about what may be called a "good death," so to speak. Likewise, when you can prepare the family, that is the start of "good grief." Someone's death is sad, and grieving is difficult. But when you have the expertise of an interdisciplinary team, as you do with hospice, it makes these occurrences much easier.

I received numerous calls and cards of appreciation from this family. I would like to say I also thank them. They allowed me, a virtual stranger, to come into their home at a most personal time in their lives. I felt like a member of this family, which made Josh's death even more sad and personal to me. People often ask me, how do I do this type of care called hospice. They wonder if it is depressing. I can say I have felt strong emotions over my years in hospice, but depression is not one of them. Have I been sad? Of course. Each patient's death is a loss to me as well. And, yes, hospice nurses do cry. But each new case renews my spirit. I'm reminded of what an awesome privilege it is to walk this journey with my patients and their families. I think that is incredibly special. Thank you, Joshua, for teaching me so much. When I look at my girls who are healthy, I will think of you and how brave you were. You and your family left an indelible mark on my memory. I'm not exactly sure where it is, but I know there must be a beautiful beach in heaven. I can picture you running along the shoreline now, Joshua. It was an honor and privilege to be with you and your family at this most personal time. Thank you.

A Boy and His Dog

She would happily greet me as I climbed up the stairs
A constant companion for this sick little boy
Tail wagging as if to urge me to hurry along
Her presence a constant source of joy

Gone were the days they could play fetch and run
At the park they both loved so well
Since illness had claimed him, his spirit grew tired
But not his love, she could tell

Her days now were filled with guarding his side
And the many soft strokes he would give
She knew things had changed, that her master was weak
And she wondered how long he would live

As days turned to weeks the house became more quiet
People she did not know would come to give care
Her master grew weary as she lay at his side
Wondering just how much longer he would be here

And so the day came that the boy took his leave
She stayed very still as she tugged on his sleeve
As if to say, "I will miss you. So glad we were friends,
I was happy to be with you right up to the end"

SHIRLEY

Shirley was an 82-year-old woman who lived alone in a row home not too far from where I live. Her hospital bed was set up in her living room against the wall. She told me she spent a lot of time in bed but could still get up to go to the kitchen to get meals. Since her bathroom was on the second floor, she used a bedside commode. Her home was a narrow row house. The lighting was poor, making it seem as if it was always nighttime. Dusty metal blinds covered the only two windows in the room. It had the distinct smell of a room that needed fresh air. It was rather cluttered, and she seemed embarrassed by that when I first met her, although I tried to put her mind at ease. I told her about our volunteer program, which included someone who could come in and help her do light cleaning as she saw fit. She said she would think about it. She was a very proud woman and was not used to asking for help. I knew this was a process that would take some time. I thought of my own childhood. Since my grandmother lived with us, there was always someone who could help her. She had companionship and love. I wished I could say the same for Shirley. My plan was to gain her trust and let her know that her well-being was my primary concern. I was not there to judge her about her living situation. My goal was to make her more comfortable and help her to understand the holistic nature of hospice care.

She was a widow whose companions were a 10-year-old border collie named Molly and a six-year-old cat named Spunky. People become very attached to their pets, especially those they've had for a long time. This was certainly the case for Shirley. Spunky could often be found curled up in Shirley's bed. He looked quite comfortable. I could tell this was a comfort to Shirley as well. "Oh yes. Spunky is my little bed partner. I've had him for almost five years. He keeps me warm too." She chuckled at that remark, and I laughed right along with her. I asked her about the dog I had seen in the backyard. It was obvious she had not been able to care for Molly for quite a while. Most of the grass had been worn down. The area was mostly dirt and needed cleaning. Shirley's affection for this animal was obvious. Her face lit up as she described her beloved Molly. It was very distressing to Shirley that she could no longer take Molly for the walks that she loved. Nor could she play with her in the backyard. Molly was outside for most of the day. At night, she was allowed in a small back porch area that was enclosed. "I miss being able to take care of Molly. I used to be able to go outside in the yard with her, but now I can't do that. I am just too sick."

I empathized with Shirley and told her that this was one thing we could talk about. I wanted her to know that if it was important to her, it was important to me. Part of my concern in formulating her care plan was how her animals would be cared for both now and after her death. The condition of her small backyard was proof that she could no longer cope with their care.

I discussed this problem with the hospice team at our weekly meeting. That's the beauty of being part of a team like ours. You can present an issue like Shirley's and benefit from the ideas of others. Our volunteer coordinator knew other volunteers who were especially fond of animals. She, in turn, recommended a few others who shared this interest. And so, the "pet volunteer group" was born. They did things such as cleaning the yard, emptying litter boxes and dog walking, relieving Shirley of the responsibility and putting her mind at ease. She often voiced concern about how her pets would be cared for. The pet volunteers planned for a forever home for Shirley's animals. There was a cat shelter willing to take Spunky, and a farmer friend of one of the volunteers said he would take Molly. He came to visit Shirley to discuss arrangements. It was agreed that the dog would visit the farm weekly and, in this way, become accustomed to the surroundings. When it came time for a permanent move, Molly would be ready. These plans lightened Shirley's heart. She could cross this worry off her list.

"Oh, I'm so happy that Molly will have all that space to run around in. This is wonderful. I had no idea a hospice program could do something like this. Thank you, Linda." Her face lit up as if someone had just given her a wonderful treasure. The news was like a gift from heaven to her.

Shirley was a frail woman who wore oxygen continuously. I especially worried about her living alone and the safety issues that might arise. When someone has an oxygen concentrator in their home, they must understand that there can be no open flames. That means they cannot smoke or burn any candles. Our medical supply company came monthly to check the functioning of the oxygen unit. I was also checking the tubing routinely to see if there were any other supplies Shirley might need. All these things could be delivered to her home. Shirley shared with me that she had been a smoker for many years but had stopped a few years ago. I arranged for one of our home health aides to come in three times a week to help Shirley with bathing, meal preparation, and other needs. Anything that had to do with her being comfortable would also be addressed. She usually stayed in her nightgown which was most comfortable for her. Her abdomen was quite distended due to an untreated umbilical hernia. It was not painful per se but did affect the type of clothing she could tolerate. Our team decided one of us would visit Shirley daily. This way someone could touch base with her and be able to address any problem that she may present to us.

You may be wondering about Shirley's family. She had a daughter, Beverly, who lived nearby but did not visit very often. After several phone calls, I was finally able to reach her. I wanted to explain the type of care her mother was going to be receiving from the hospice team. Our social worker had met with Shirley and her daughter to sign the necessary consents to start services. Since I was not part of that initial visit, I had not met Beverly in person. I asked her if she had any questions. Had she been familiar with home hospice care prior to now? Did she have any concerns about how her mother's course of illness might play out? I asked if she had spoken with the physician about her mother's prognosis. She explained to me that she and her mother were not very close. "Mom has always been pretty independent. She only tells me what she wants me to know. So, I guess I stopped asking. I did speak to her doctor a few times and it did answer some questions." This was good information for me as I went about trying to support Beverly. Considering these difficult family dynamics, my approach was a little bit different. I had to respect Shirley's independence. I also would be respectful about giving Beverly information without Shirley's knowledge. Confidentiality is always respected with our patients, in most cases close family members are part of that circle. With Beverly, this was not the case. There could be no assumptions on my part that this was a typical mother-daughter relationship. Again, I pause to think of my own mother. Since I worked full time as a hospice nurse during her terminal illness, my visits were not as frequent as I would have liked. I would have given anything to live as close to my mother as Beverly did to Shirley. This reminded me we are all individuals. It reminded me of a phrase I had thought of often: "You must meet the patient and their family where they are, not where you want them to be."

As her condition declined, Shirley stayed in bed most of the time. She rarely got out except to use the commode which was at her bedside. Her daughter had now been calling daily. I spoke to Beverly more frequently, trying to impress upon her that Shirley's prognosis was most likely just a few weeks. I knew how I would feel in this situation. I had to keep reminding myself that this was a different circumstance than I had experienced with my own mother. I said a little prayer for patience and wisdom as I tried to have Beverly understand the gravity of the situation. After some coaxing, she agreed to start coming every evening and stay the night. This way she could respond to her mother if she needed something during the evening and night hours. This put my mind at ease. Family dynamics are a curious thing. You must know who will respond to the call when the extra help is needed.

Relationships that have been formed prior to our patient's illness do not suddenly change when a person goes on hospice care. The nurse in me fully understood the dynamics playing out here, but the daughter in me wished for something different. Shirley mentioned that her daughter had a new boyfriend. "I'm pretty sure that's why she doesn't want to come over to my house and stay very long." I honestly did not know how to answer this comment. "Well, surely, you know, you can always talk to Beverly about this." She just raised her eyebrows and shook her head. Beverly had a part time job as a secretary and had no children. I have learned that each family has a unique story, not all of them pleasant. As her hospice nurse, my hope was that her daughter would see her mother's decline and be more of a presence in her life. This would be her decision. My hope for her was that she knew whatever time she gave to her mother now would be well worth it. She would have to live with whatever choices she made now. This was the time for her to make some final memories with her mother. I hope she realized that. "Shirley, if you have any pictures you might want to share with Beverly, I can help you find them." Shirley said if her daughter wanted to do this, that would be okay with her. Neither of them seemed very enthusiastic about the idea. But I felt I had to at least make this suggestion.

Speaking of pictures, I noticed one very old photograph on a bookcase in the room where Shirley slept. She told me that it was she and her brother. It was taken when they were both very young children. He lived in upstate New York and was a retired bookkeeper. He tried to visit about once a month. It seemed they were rather close, as he was Shirley's only sibling, and she looked forward to his visits. I asked if I could call him and introduce myself to see if he had any questions. She said he was aware she was receiving hospice care. "Oh, that would be very nice. I know Charlie is worried about me and wondering how I am doing. He has tried to reach my daughter but said she is never at home when he calls. He does understand what hospice is, so I'm sure he would love to talk to you." Shirley gave me Charlie's phone number, and I promised I would call that same day.

On one visit, I noticed Shirley's cat was lying in bed with her. Spunky was a black cat with a distinctive white marking behind his right ear. When I asked how old he was Shirley was not sure. "He was actually a stray that I took in. That was over five years ago. He was probably a few years old at that time."

"I guess once he touched your heart, he had found a forever home," I said to her. She smiled and nodded in agreement, "Oh yes, with Spunky and Molly. We are quite a nice little family." As I mentioned before, Shirley had this untreated hernia. That caused a great protrusion under the covers. It did not cause her any pain and she had decided many years ago not to have it treated. During one visit, I turned toward the bed to see Spunky gently massaging that area. The cat was very calm and seemed to be concentrating on the task at hand. Spunky was never taught this. That was remarkable and lasted almost the entire visit. When the task was complete. He curled up next to his mistress and gave a slow long purr. Yes, it was a job well done.

Shirley's death was uneventful. She was comfortable and asymptomatic. Her concerns for the animals were relieved. Her daughter was able to discuss some financial matters with her, and so she was ready to go on her journey. She had shared with me that she felt she lived a good life. I heard stories about her many years as a crossing guard for the neighborhood children. "They were like the grandchildren I never had," she said proudly.

This was a particularly ironic story for me. You see, my own mother had been a crossing guard in our neighborhood for over 30 years. I still have an old newspaper article where she was given a plaque of appreciation for her long service along with a beautiful bouquet of flowers. Like Shirley, she enjoyed talking with the children as they came to and from school. She used to tell me stories about how they shared their day with her. I truly believe she was like a grandmother to most of them as well. Shirley remembered when one of her charges found out it was her birthday. He brought her a small bouquet of flowers. She also received the most perfect homemade birthday cards, the kind only children can make. She shared with me that this was one of her best birthdays. I could almost hear my mother speaking. When Shirley said this to me, "I was kind of like their guardian Angel. At least they were safe walking to and from school," it was clear that this was more than a job to Shirley. She took great pride in keeping her charges safe. It may not seem like a great accomplishment to some, but to Shirley it was a noble cause. I feel the same way about my own mother and her role as a crossing guard in our small town. Thank you to both.

This case was a success story in making plans for a person's animals prior to their death. I would like to say that this is the case most of the time. Unfortunately, there are too many cases when this has not happened. In those circumstances, the local animal shelter will be called to help place the animal. With Shirley, her animals provided the love and attention she needed and did not get from her daughter. Animals give love unconditionally. The same thing cannot be said of some humans. I believe this was the case for Shirley and her daughter. Whatever circumstances came into their lives, this relationship did not bloom as a loving one. But Shirley had no doubts that Molly and Spunky loved her. They brought her sheer joy and the knowledge that she was not alone.

Shirley's life wasn't a perfect one, but she had no regrets. She really taught me the value of ordinary things. Like how animals can give love. I think of her whenever I pass by her home or see a border collie or a cat that looks like Spunky. I recently heard from one of our volunteers that kept in touch with the farmer who adopted Molly. The border collie had died that week. I know that she was met by Shirley on the Rainbow Bridge. What a joyful meeting that must have been! I can picture Shirley running with Molly without her oxygen. It made me glad that our hospice team was so instrumental in making the plans to have these animals cared for. That was the final gift that we gave to Shirley. And I know she was grateful. Allowing us to do this for her was her gift to us. Thank you, Shirley, Molly and Spunky.

A Different Kind of Family

She lived alone in a small city house
But to say she was lonely would not be true
The smile on her face told the whole story
Of her dog and her cat, her very special two

Spunky the cat could often be found snuggled in bed
Keeping his favorite gal warm
Molly, the collie, waited outside for her turn to visit
As this was the promise that was sworn

"I just love my little family," she would say
These three would make my heart warm
I promised I would find both of them good homes
Much too soon, she would be gone

It rested heavily on my shoulders
As I prayed about what to do
The answer came when a man with a farm
was willing to see this through

I pictured the grassy fields, and an old red barn
So many places for an animal to roam
Add the love of this newfound stranger
And soon they were calling it "home"

I brought her the newsof this treasure I'd found
And her smile was as big as the sky!
She could now be at peace, for her family was safe
She could now say her final goodbye

In the weeks that ensued, I went to the farm
I vowed I would check on these two
It was clear, they were healthy, and happy
They had found a home that was true

Before I left, I turned for one final glance
I know I saw Shirley's face
She was sitting on a nearby swing
Watching them with that same smile on her face

The vision quickly faded
But it was enough for me to know
They I had kept my promise
And she was free to go

MATTHEW

This next case was especially emotional for our team. A certain feeling would permeate our office when a referral came in for a newborn or small infant. They have barely lived and now they're dying. From the moment we knew his name, he was our little Angel. People often seem surprised when they hear that there are small infants or little children receiving hospice care. As a society, we usually think as death striking only the elderly and infirm. The thought of such a little one being given a terminal prognosis goes against everything that most of us feel death should be. Elderly patients with debilitating chronic diseases or end stage cancer somehow seem more acceptable to us. You often hear the phrase "they've lived a good life". But what is to be said of such a little one whom I am about to tell you about? We often hear accounts of parents bargaining with God. Asking for just one more day, or month, or year, somehow blaming themselves for the illnesses of their little ones. Was something missed by the doctor? Should they have sought medical care sooner. If it happens to be a genetic disease, there is tremendous guilt on the part of both parents about their decision to have a child. All these circumstances present themselves as part of the bigger picture. The journey from diagnosis to hospice care to the dying process has its twists and turns. As a hospice team our various members have the expertise to help our families navigate this rough road. Here is one particularly poignant story.

Matthew was just three days old. He was born with a gastric condition that did not allow food to pass through his gastrointestinal track. It also did not allow a feeding tube to be placed. His parents were a loving young couple of 17 and 19 years old, Maria and Teddy. I can't even imagine the heartache they were suffering. First the news of an infant so ill, then the news that there were no surgeries or treatments available to help him. He would be brought home to be cared for by his loving family. Our hospice team would provide support and guidance, whatever that may mean. We met as a team as we always did to formulate what is called a patient care plan. There are special circumstances when an infant is involved. Especially when considering the emotional needs of such a young couple. We made it known immediately that we were available 24/7. As with all our families, we urged that Maria and Teddy call anytime of the day or night with any concerns or worries they may have. They understood and promised us they would. At the same time, we made it known that we valued their privacy and their need to have as much time as possible with little Matthew.

Matthew had a large extended family. They would visit frequently. Each one held the baby and offered love and support to the young parents. Our chaplain and social worker spoke to each one also. Lending guidance is their area of expertise. It is often a balance between knowing when to counsel through words and sometimes through silence. The gift of presence is a valuable one.

One thing that weighed heavy on Maria's mind was that she wanted Matthew to be baptized. With all the attention that was given to his physical health, this need was still unfulfilled. The team decided very quickly that we would arrange for this to happen as soon as possible. I would bake a cake and another nurse bought a baptism outfit for the baby. Our chaplain would perform the ceremony. Because his prognosis was so poor, we decided to gather at the home the next day to hold the baptism. We were happy to enact this new special plan. Matthew was dedicated to God, and his mother said she felt a sense of peace. We were so glad to be able to do this for this wonderful family. Hospice care is holistic in nature. Along with addressing physical and psychological needs, spiritual concerns are extremely important. Faith often plays an integral part in how a family copes with the news of a terminal illness. The presence of God or a higher being may give added strength and assist families in dealing with the difficulties they are facing.

At this point in his care, I visited Matthew daily. He was asymptomatic and seemed comfortable at this point. I talked with Maria and Teddy about how the next few days might play out as she watched her baby's condition decline. I wanted them to understand that changes would happen very quickly. I answered their questions and allowed them to express any fears or concerns they may have had at that time. As parents they needed to know they were doing everything exactly right. And I would tell them that many times when Teddy was quieter. I realized he needed his space at this most difficult time. It's not always easy to know how to offer hope or encouragement in such a sad circumstance. But the hospice team always did their best to act with love and honesty and coming to terms with your feelings is also important. You won't always have the answers. I have been asked if, as a hospice nurse, do I cry in front of patients and families. The answer is, of course I do. That is part of honesty, part of my being human. As a professional, I bring with me every experience I have had in the past. These are what I draw from as I learn something unique from each case.

Since the infant could not retain any nutrition, we knew his prognosis was grave. He was given a pacifier to help soothe him. His mother held him continually. He had quite a healthy head of dark hair. His tiny fingers grasped his mother's. I would have to say he was content. It was as if special angels were sent to attend him and gather round him to give his mother strength as well as she held him. His father Teddy looked over his tiny family not unlike Joseph looking over Mary and Jesus in that tiny stable. Their love and devotion to each other was palpable. Each person supported these young parents in their own way. Our chaplain and social worker spoke to each one lending guidance. It is often a balance between knowing when to counsel through words and sometimes through silence. As I said earlier, the gift of presence is a valuable one. This is a lesson I would like to share with you. Words may escape you when you are visiting a terminally ill friend or family member. There are times when just your being there speaks volumes. A gentle touch will let the person know that you are there for them. It will also let family members and caregivers know they don't have to be pressured to speak. I'm sure you have all heard the saying "silence is golden." In my many years doing hospice work I have found this to be true.

Matthew was given a prognosis of only a week at home. Each day, each minute, of his short life he knew he was loved. Our chaplain visited often and prayed together with Maria and

Teddy. I was on call the early morning that Matthew started his final journey. In hospice we believe there are no coincidences. I feel it was preordained that I would be the one on call when Matthew died. I would be the one to go to the home and pronounce the death and support this extraordinary family I had come to know. Pronouncement of death is the technical term for saying that the person has no vital signs, and life as we know it has left them. The hospice nurse determines that death has occurred, but it is the physician who determines the cause of death.

It was around 2:00 AM on a cold snowy, dark winter's night when I received the call. Since I had visited the home many times the ride was a familiar one. But there was a different feel to my trip this time. I knew it would be the last time I would be visiting Matthew and his family in their home. Matthew had already died when I got there. Maria and Teddy shared his last moments with love and tenderness. I could tell they felt good about being able to bring their little boy home and have him be surrounded by family for these few short days. If circumstances allow, it is very beneficial to have a person die at home. Discharge planners are well informed about this type of care and can assist with the process.

Maria and Teddy asked if our chaplain could officiate at Matthews funeral service. Of course, he consented. We all attended the celebration of this angel's life. And yes, we all cried. We offered support to this young couple. Stories were shared and Matthew was remembered as a little boy who brought so much love in such a brief time. He gave his parents such joy. After the death of their loved one, families are followed in bereavement for the next year and a half. This is part of the hospice program for each bereaved family. Contact is maintained for that time period so that families know that support is available to whomever may need it. Grief is a very personal process, and no two people grieve in the same way. A bereavement coordinator completes an evaluation which determines the level of contact hospice families require. Follow-up can range from phone calls on a predetermined schedule to a visit from the coordinator. Most hospices also offer support groups that are facilitated by bereavement counselors. If an issue is detected during a routine call, the counselor may recommend private help to the bereaved. Where there are siblings, special support groups may be recommended.

So, what was the lesson I learned from Matthew during his short journey from serious illness to death? This tiny little one touched so many lives in such a short time. I learned the power of the love of a parent. I was taught the importance of faith, whatever that might mean to an individual. And lastly, I learned the value of each life lived, no matter how short that life might be. It has a lasting effect on those left behind. Everyone whose life Matthew touched were better people for his being in their lives and they will never be the same. I know I won't. I was able to walk the last part of his journey on earth. And that's a gift that is invaluable.

The Littlest Angel

Tiny little baby, no bigger than a breath
Your time on Earth has not been long
God sent you to teach us to love, keep faith
And always be strong

Your mother holds you, oh so close
As your father kisses your cheek
They know you are like a fleeting star
One they would so love to keep

But the Angels are waiting for you to come home
Even though you've not had much time
A miracle happened the day you were born
Every breath you took was like a rhyme

You taught us how to love and care
With each heartbeat, you stayed strong
It may have been a fleeting life
But to us, you will always belong

With pain and tears, I will let you go
Heaven will now be your home
Until we meet on that special day
When you no longer will be alone

I will look for you in the rising sun
In the shadow of the moon
I will see your face in each new cloud
The rain will sing you a tune

So, hold on, precious Angel boy
You are truly a chosen one
Your love will be my sustenance
Until my life is done

JOHN

My next account will introduce you to John, a retired dentist. His terminal diagnosis was ALS, amyotrophic lateral sclerosis, commonly known as Lou Gehrig's disease. As many of you may know, Lou Gehrig was a famous baseball player who contracted this disease. His illness is well documented. John was familiar with this famous athlete. This fact lent an air of familiarity in talking about what John may be facing. Mr. Gehrig's disease was played out on the baseball diamond. It served as a learning tool for others who would contract it. He was a fighter and made it clear he would go on as long as he could. I soon learned this was true for John as well.

John lived in a lovely two-story home with his wife Carol. She was a dedicated caregiver. Her friendly disposition made it easy for her to accept the help that our team had to offer. She was very familiar with hospice care as one of her close friends had received it about a year earlier. It was clear to me our team would soon be treated as part of the family. After all, what is more personal than being part of someone's life during the dying process? I cannot think of many circumstances that would fit that description. "How do you think John will feel about different people coming into his home to help him?" I inquired. He was sleeping when I first arrived, so I posed this question to Carol to get an idea of the man. "Well, John is not one for long conversation, but he will always give you an honest answer and tell you what he needs." I told her I thought that sounded like a good place to start. She quipped that may have been from his years of tending to people in his chair who could not converse while he was treating them. That made us smile.

John soon woke up, and I introduced myself. I let him know the reason for my visit. "Did your doctor tell you much about what home hospice would be like, John?" I asked.

"Well, he told me a few things. I knew there would be a nurse coming. I guess that's you, and other folks could come in as long as I said they could." I assured him that that was the case. He would be making these decisions about how his care would be carried out. It seemed it was more difficult for John to accept help than his wife. Here was another professional who was accustomed to being in charge. He had his own private practice for more than 25 years. His office staff consisted of four to five people at any given time. Learning to accept the hospice team was a learning curve for him.

Each visit brought John closer to the realization that we were all there to help him and Carol. That's an important concept to convey to our patients from the very beginning of their care. They have lost so much independence regarding everyday life. They need to know they are respected and their opinions matter. We are the professionals of the medical community ready to care for these patients, but first and foremost we are guests in their homes. John was often asleep or receiving care from the hospice aide when I arrived. She would help him shower and shave and get dressed and make him breakfast. "Can I have the occupational therapist come in to do a safety check in the bathroom, John? There might be some equipment he can recommend which would help you navigate a little easier. If you agree to this, I can order this from our medical equipment company, and it will be covered under the hospice benefit. There is no charge to you." He agreed the plan would be fine with him. He appreciated the fact that it would be covered by the hospice benefit. I made the necessary calls to the doctor for the order, referring the occupational therapist. Once it was decided what John would need, he would call the equipment company to be delivered to the home as soon as possible.

The other important focus of my visits was speaking with John's wife, Carol. At times she was just waking up. I would call out that I had arrived, and she would urge me to come upstairs. "I'm still in bed, Linda. Grab a cup of coffee if you want." I told her I would, if I could bring her one as well. "One cream and one sugar, right, Carol?" She verified the order, and I poured the coffee and went upstairs to the bedroom. At her urging, it was not unusual for me to kick off my shoes and sit on the bed. She started to share information about John's night. I marveled at her calm demeanor. Here was the woman facing the inevitable death of her husband. Her attitude of acceptance made my conversations with her very natural. This began a very special relationship between Carol and me. This is what hospice nurses do. We formulate relationships that grow as we meet the needs of our patients and their families and caregivers.

This is how our morning meetings would go. Carol would tell me how John's days had gone since my last visit. "How has John been sleeping in the last few nights?" I asked. She reported that he was sleeping a little better since starting the new medication. I had called the physician to see about ordering a sleeping pill for John. He agreed. It seemed that medication really made a difference. "Let's face it, if John doesn't sleep, I don't sleep. That makes for a grouchy wife in the morning." We both laughed and conceded that this was probably true.

Next, I would inquire about John's breathing. At this point he was using the oxygen all night and at periods during the day when he needed it. "Will John ask for the oxygen to be put on if he needs it, Carol?" I inquired. "He will for the most part. I do have to say though, there are times when I will walk into the room, and I can see he is struggling to breathe. I offer to put the oxygen on, and he usually accepts it." The hospice aide had been instructed to offer to put on John's oxygen after his shower and any other time he seemed exhausted or short of breath. Along with the oxygen, Carol was taught to administer liquid morphine to help with the difficult breathing as well. The action of morphine causes a person's breathing to become slower and more regular. Doses are started at a low level and increased as needed per the order of the physician. I would call him with updates and to inquire about changing medication depending on what symptoms John was presenting with. It was an easy professional give and take. I had demonstrated to Carol how to measure the proper dose of that medication in a small syringe that had the dose marked on the side. This was the most accurate way to draw up the liquid medication and administer it to John.

The conversation would then turn to Carol. I wanted to speak with her about her role as the wife and the partner, the person who stood by her husband's side through any adversity that life may have given them. "What are the things that keep you up at night? "I asked her. She answered that one of her biggest anxieties was not hearing John if he should need her. In the past month, he had taken to sleeping in the recliner in the next room. Being able to be in an upright position facilitated easier breathing for him. "I know he's only in the next room, but it still makes me scared." I acknowledge her fears and say I'd probably feel the same way. Of course, she felt scared.

"The thought that John might need me during the night, and I would not hear him is just too much to even think of," she remarked. I first gave this practical advice. I thought of similar cases where patients had respiratory conditions. Their caregivers had a lot of these same worries. One family got a small bell that the person could ring if they needed something. Others used a baby monitor. Our hospice program has donations of these and are very glad to lend them to families. I offered this as a possible solution to Carol.

I still wanted to know more about how she was feeling. I asked her how she thought she would handle saying goodbye to her spouse of over 40 years. She knew she was doing all she possibly could and had a strong faith that would help her greatly.

"I know when the time comes that God calls John home, I will be ready. There are so many people in our church praying for John. I pray that he does not struggle, that he is ready himself when the time comes. If that can happen, my own prayers will have been answered."

We then talked about other support systems. She and John had two daughters who both lived out of state. She described them as great kids.

"We talk on the phone almost every day. Even if John is too weak to speak, I let him hear the girls. This is a great joy to him and it really lifts his spirits. They try to visit more often now and are getting ready to take some vacation so they can come home soon before they need to."

I knew exactly what Carol meant. Families who do not live near their dying family members often ask me about when to visit if they come home while the person is alive they won't be able to afford to come to the funeral. For some, this is just a stark reality. I tell them, of course the decision is theirs. The question to think of is this: Do I want to come now for a visit and possibly a conversation with my loved one? Or do I feel I need to be at the funeral service with my other family members and relatives? There is no right or wrong answer. Like any difficult decision, you must choose the one that will leave you at peace. Our social worker had contacted both girls to offer support and let them know how hospice was there for the whole family. She explained to them that if they felt the need, she could refer them to a hospice in their hometown. This was not unusual in cases where family members did not live nearby. Right now, they were fine with a phone call from our team members. They would certainly let us know if they changed their mind.

Clinically, the course of ALS is predictable. Of course, patients go through different phases differently. One thing that was inevitable was that respirations would become very difficult as the disease progressed. In simple terms, this means that a person will be short of breath more often and need more oxygen and more medication. John and Carol had already had the conversation about intubation and being put on a respirator. Both agreed this was not something they wanted John to go through. Medically speaking, one would say that he was a "do not resuscitate," a DNR as it is termed. I report this because it is not something that automatically happens. Spouses, caregivers, families, and anyone else involved in a person's care can have very differing opinions as to the decision to sign a DNR. This is where the presence of a living will or advanced directive can be invaluable. If discussions about antibiotics, intravenous medications, or other treatments surface, these decisions are already made. It is then up to the medical power of attorney to see they are honored. This disease is overwhelming and can put strain on a relationship. If a couple has these difficult conversations, however, these preplanned decisions make all the difference in the world. John and Carol were able to do just that. I asked them both if this was a difficult decision. Carol said she would honor John's wishes. Whatever they were, they both learned all they could at the initial diagnosis of his ALS. Breathing issues and respirators were something clearly discussed in all the literature.

"Well, I knew that was going to happen eventually, and I really don't want to be on a machine, so I guess I'm leaving it to the man upstairs." These were John's words, and Carol nodded in approval. "That pretty much says it. We've always made important decisions together. And that isn't going to change now. No tubes or respirators."

As I have remarked earlier, this is where the benefit of having a hospice involved with your loved ones care is invaluable. Regardless of a caregiver's background or profession, when a family member is sick, it is a different story. In my own family, my father had a history of severe congestive heart failure or CHF. This condition is such that it can exacerbate every few months. During one of his hospitalizations, I sat and watched my father struggle for breath. It seemed that I was split into two emotionally. Part of me was that hospice nurse that knew exactly what to do. The other part was his daughter, who just wanted to scream. His symptoms were attended to quickly, and he did get relief. His primary nurse that day was someone that I knew. She told me that this was the time for me to be a daughter first, not a nurse. Of course, we cannot deny what we know, but it is a time for we professionals to yield to those caring for our loved ones. In other words, I really needed to take my own advice. I spent the rest of my visit sitting quietly, remembering my other lesson of the value of presence.

As John's breathing became more difficult, medication doses were changed after consulting his physician. Try to imagine if this were you sitting there next to your loved one, watching his breathing patterns change. You are wondering if what you're going to do is going to help. And yet feeling so helpless yourself. I received the new dosage orders from the doctor. This was done so that the maximum comfort level could be achieved for John. I mentioned morphine being used to help ease breathing and control pain. Lorazepam, also called Ativan, is also ordered to help ease anxiety. This also facilitates easier breathing and more comfortable sleep. John's oxygen needed to be increased at this point. With all these changes in place, he began to feel more relaxed. Our aides are taught about these symptoms, which many of our patients present with, so they can call the primary hospice nurse or supervisor to report these changes and this way symptoms can be dealt with in a timely manner. All new aides complete a specially designed course on caring for the hospice patient. I personally have instructed the unit on pain management for health aides. I've never seen a more dedicated group of caregivers. Carol also knew that she could call anytime of the day or night to report a change and to get help. That meant even a visit in the middle of the night. "Knowing that I can call and get help and even a nurse would come here at night is such a relief to me. I hope everybody that's in our situation knows about hospice. You really don't feel alone."

Our hospice chaplain started to visit more frequently, as did John's own pastor. This allowed John time to discuss any spiritual concerns he may have had. He valued the privacy and the chance to talk one-on-one with another man. "I appreciate everything all you ladies do, but sometimes I just need to talk to a man." He gave a kind of half smile, and I did as well. The chaplain can often put to rest unanswered questions of faith that bring concerns to a patient. Also, from a practical aspect, there is the matter of the funeral service. Often if the patient does not have their own clergy to perform their funeral ritual, they may request our hospice chaplain to officiate. The social worker plays an important part with the funeral arrangements as well. She may make calls for the patient or help family with decisions regarding exactly what they would like the funeral service to portray.

John shared an interesting request that he had made of a very close friend of his. Sam was a carpenter by trade and John thought it would be a great idea if he would build a simple casket, which would be John's final resting place. Having gotten to know John well, this did not surprise me. John was the type of person that got right to the point. Whatever the discussion involved, he shared with his friend exactly what this should look like. The type of wood, the type of stain, the hardware to be used. Nothing was to be fancy, simply something sturdy to stand the test of time. I have never experienced this type of request before, and I thought it was a wonderful gift from one close friend to another. Sam made a few visits in the next few weeks. I allowed these two their privacy to complete these very special plans.

Another few days went by, and it was clear that John had turned a corner. Both his daughters had come home and were able to spend quality time at his bedside. With Carol joining the circle, they did some life review about their childhood and some of the funny things their father had done. This is exactly how it should be, I thought. John died peacefully which was his and Carol's wish. He was fortunate to have his wife and daughters present there. For those families that cannot be present in person, we recommend that a phone call be done. Even if it's clear the person cannot speak. We know that hearing is the last sense to leave us. Wouldn't it be nice to hear a loved one's voice as the last thing you have heard?

The funeral was much in keeping with this private man that I had come to know. The handmade pine box was so eloquently crafted, exactly as I expected it to be. It was wheeled into the church as John's favored hymns were being played. Sam had kept his promise to his close friend. I'm sure John was smiling. Somehow, I feel I could just hear him saying to Sam, "Job well done. Thank you, my friend."

Carol expressed many thanks to the hospice team. This is a phrase that I often use about partners and family members regarding their loved one's death: "She was both saddened and relieved." Certainly very sad at having to say goodbye to the love of her life, her confidant and partner. But then again, relieved, John was now set free. He was no longer short of breath, he was no longer suffering, and he had gone back to God. Carol's faith told her that and brought her great comfort.

There's a certain sense of fulfillment about a case that unfolds as John's did. I would say he had a good death and isn't that exactly the way hospice care should be? John and Carol taught me the importance of communication and honesty and the possibility of having difficult conversations. Their willingness to allow our team to assist them was really a gift to all of us. The love they shared for each other was palpable, and I thanked them for showing this to us with such great ease and sincerity.

A Simple Man

His strength was in his silence
One look and it was clear
He had a plan to follow
The end was very near

The one that he had cherished
Forever at his side
She gave him peace and loving care
In her heart he would abide

No need for glitz or fancy stuff
As he planned his resting place
A simple box made by a dear old friend
Would surely fit his taste

I watched as family gathered
To say their last farewell
Elegant in its simplicity
What stories it could tell

I sent him off with words of thanks
For I was humbled too
And caring for this simple man
I learned how to be true

TUYET

Each patient I had in hospice has taught me valuable lessons which have served me well in my life. So it was with my elderly patient, Tuyet. She was a ninety-six-year-old Vietnamese woman who spoke no English. Since I did not speak Vietnamese, her daughter and son-in-law served as translators. I learned that it is important to face the person you are speaking with, even though they do not understand your language. It shows respect that you are speaking with them even though someone else is translating. Respect was a very important part of Tuyet's culture.

Tuyet lived with her family and their 18-month-old daughter Lily in a modest bi-level home. Her bedroom was in the back of the house, a simple room with soft colors. A statue of Buddha was displayed on the dresser. I would learn this was the religion that Tuyet and her family followed. In my caring for her, I learned a great deal about Buddhism as the days and weeks went by. This culture showed great respect for Tuyet as the eldest family member. Their entire home had an air of respect. Everyone spoke quietly and walked gently. Even simple tasks were done with great respect and purpose. I observed that as I watched her son-in-law help her with her meal. He moved slowly and purposefully. It was as if this was the most important thing he had to do. And I believe it was. "I can see your mother-in-law is very special to you," I remarked. "Oh yes, it is my honor to be able to serve her." I would see over the coming days that this attitude permeated everything that was done while caring for this most important person.

Tuyet was a petite woman with soft blue eyes. Her face showed traces of a person who had led a life of hard work. I learned that she worked on a large property where her family raised vegetables, which were then sold at a local market. She was married at age 16 at a traditional Vietnamese wedding. From what I have learned, there are three different ceremonies prior to the actual wedding ceremony. These include the permission ceremony, when both families first meet. The betrothal or engagement ceremony, and finally the wedding. Everything is quite ornate and well planned. "That is so interesting," I told her. "Thank you for explaining all this to me. It is so different from here in the United States."

Her daughter, Bian, with whom she lived, told me she had three siblings: a sister, Cai, and two brothers, Liam and Hoa. They still lived in Vietnam. They corresponded mostly by letter, as phone calls were too costly. Bian made sure her siblings were kept abreast of their mother's condition. They could share any important information with the rest of the family in Vietnam.

Tuyet had a diagnosis of metastatic liver cancer. The exact secondary site was not clear, but it was thought to be in her bones. "Bone pain can be quite severe," I explained to Bian and her husband Philip. Adequate pain management and symptom control are two of the primary goals the hospice nurse has for her patients. We strive to be familiar with the latest modalities. One way this is achieved is by becoming a certified Hospice Palliative Care Nurse. This is referred to with the acronym CHPN. Being certified in any nursing specialty gives that clinician the latest information to supplement her knowledge base. The word palliative refers to a person's symptoms being eased or palliated. In some cases, even relieved completely. That goal is more easily achieved in some patients than others.

"How is your pain today, Tuyet? Are you taking the pain medicine?" I asked. As I spoke, I sat in a chair near to the bed and made eye contact with her as I was speaking. Then I turned to her daughter as she and her mother were speaking in Vietnamese. Bian reported that her mother's pain was well controlled at this time. I reminded her to offer the medicine to her mother. Sometimes patients are reluctant to ask for pain medication. Families can be instrumental in helping them achieve a desirable comfort level.

There are some circumstances where a numeric scale— 1 to 10—cannot be used to rate pain. In the case of dementia or other cognitive disabilities, the nurse relies on her observation of the patient's body language and changes in vital signs. This also holds true for people with a language barrier. In a case such as this, the family is instrumental in reporting the patient's comfort level. I was reminded of my own grandmother who lived with us. She was originally from Italy. She spoke some English and always had one of us nearby when her doctor would make house calls. Since he spoke her language, it made these visits very comfortable for her. I was able to understand most of what my grandmother said in Italian, but to my dismay, I never really learned to speak the language. When a physician truly understands his patients' needs, he has much more success in reaching the treatment goals he has set for the patient. In turn, his patients feel confident that their best interests are being addressed.

The demeanor of Tuyet's family was usually calm and low key. Most Vietnamese see death as a natural phase of the life cycle and elder adults are highly respected as part of their culture. Aging and death may not conjure up as many negative connotations as in western cultures. Being aware of a patient and their families' choices regarding a particular nationality, religious practice, or background will certainly assist the hospice nurse when discussing the topics of death and dying.

Tuyet's family's beliefs were based on the teachings of Confucius and Taoism from China, as well as the traditions of Buddhism. Generally, Buddhist teaching views life and death as a continuum. The belief is that consciousness continues after death and a person may be reborn. This is also called the person's spirit. Death can be an opportunity for liberation from the cycle of life, death, and rebirth. It was a unique experience to learn how this family viewed the illness and impending death of their beloved elder.

Since I could not verbally communicate with this patient, I made sure to make eye contact when speaking with her. Even though family members conveyed what information was needed, the patient was still the center of the visit. I learned to read her facial expressions and her muscle tone, especially in her extremities. She would become visibly tense when she experienced pain or discomfort, which didn't happen very often during my visits. I could also detect a change in her vital signs on occasion. Her family reported that she was worried about certain things that mattered in her life. She voiced these concerns to them, they then shared them with me. What would happen to her family after her death? Would her children remain successful and happy? Her husband had died many years ago when her children were quite young. That meant she raised them as a single parent. "I am a single parent also, Tuyet." I touched her arm to get her attention, so that she would know I was speaking with her. Her daughter translated into Vietnamese as I spoke. "I understand how difficult it can be, raising children on your own. From what I can see, you did an excellent job." The son-in-law she lived with was a pharmacist. Her daughter had been a teacher but was now happy to stay at home caring for Lily.

Tuyet's other children, who still reside in Vietnam, were all successful. They were all doing very well running their businesses. Another concern which was extremely important to her was the matter of returning her remains to the temple in her beloved city of VanDuc. Her children reassured her that they would certainly do that. They had already spoken to their family in Vietnam, so the event would go smoothly once Tuyet died. I watched her face as her daughter relayed this information to her. I could see the tension flow out of it and a soft smile appear as she closed her eyes in relief, letting out a long sigh.

I started each visit in the living room, speaking with family members. I spoke to Bian and Phillip. They were able to update me on the changes in their mother's condition since my last visit. The youngest family member greeted me with squeals and a smile only a child can give. Lily sat in her highchair while I spoke with her parents. Her laughing was a sharp contrast to the lethargic state of her grandmother in the next room. "Hello Lily, you are such a happy little girl." She started to kick her legs up and down and wave her arms as if to acknowledge my compliment. I reached in my nursing bag and pulled out a rubber glove. The child watched every step I was taking. To her delight, this foreign piece of rubber turned into a balloon, which looked something like a bird. I drew on eyes and some feathers. I am no artist, this was clear. "Here you go, Lily, this is for you." She squealed with delight as she looked toward her mother for approval. This was a brief, lighthearted moment that we all enjoyed. Children have a way of reminding us that life is still around us and will go on through them. As I turned back to the adults, I remember thinking that no matter what the culture, the adults in this home were in that "sandwich generation," caring for both their aged mother, who was dying, and their young toddler, who was just beginning. Life illustrated that very clearly. She was a welcome distraction to her parents as they went about their daily routine. It was clear to me that this family considered it an honor to be caring for their dying mother.

As a part of the plan of care, which guides the team in decision making for each patient, funeral plans are always addressed. This does not mean that every family knows exactly what they or the patient wants. In this case, as I have previously mentioned, plans had been initiated. Our chaplain visited to offer support and see if the family wanted a Buddhist priest to visit the home. They indicated they did not need any assistance. They would be following Buddhist traditions as they made plans for two months. Other family members were contacted, so they knew that her condition was rapidly declining. Tuyet had started sleeping more. She also had started talking about family members that had already died. This account was typical of what I would hear from family members whose loved ones had started the dying process. She said her husband had come to her in a dream and was waiting for her. This seemed to calm her.

We in hospice believe that no one truly dies alone. Someone comes for each dying person as they transition into the next life. Tuyet's Buddhist religion also told her that when you die, you do not go somewhere else, but rather you are reborn as something and someone completely different. I found this very comforting. It seemed that this type of belief allowed Tuyet to be the peaceful person she was, even in dying. Her Buddhist faith brought her a unique type of calm I have not seen in other patients.

Tuyet died on a sunny afternoon with several family members at her bedside. I was called to make the final visit to pronounce her death. The difference in this culture compared to so many others I had witnessed struck me immediately. I found somber faces chanting what I believe were prayers. No one was crying or showing any type of emotion. I found out later this was part of what is called "the farewell."

According to Buddhist tradition, family members would all gather at the house of the deceased on the seventh day following the death. This is where the family believes the soul of the deceased will visit. They stay in their rooms and powder is sprinkled around the door to confirm their presence. Any crying that would be done would have to wait until after the loved one had been taken out of the home.

Another part of this ritual was that the loved one had to remain undisturbed for four hours. This was to allow time for the spirit to leave the body. I was also told that some families have a mourning period of 49 days, as they believe this is how long rebirth takes. During this time, they say prayers for the deceased every seven days to help them pass into the next life. This was one of the most respectful family presences I have ever witnessed. Everyone knew their place and what was acceptable. It brought a sense of calm reverence to every task performed in caring for this most special person.

I attended the funeral, which was a glorious celebration compared to the solemn atmosphere at Tuyet's home when she died. She was dressed in bright colors of red and gold. There was a procession of family members making their way towards the casket. The atmosphere was festive. There were no rows of chairs with people sitting and crying. This may be in part because Buddhists believe that reincarnation of the soul takes place after death. Flowers, fruit, candles, and a portrait of the deceased were placed in front of the casket. The scent of a unique type of incense filled the room. Buddhist funeral rites vary, but in general there is an altar to the deceased person and an image of Buddha is placed there. Monks usually oversee a time of meditation, and the body is cremated after the service.

The immediate family wore white headbands and were dressed entirely in white. One person carried a bell which kept time for the procession. One held a wooden block which they hit with a precise rhythm. A large picture of Buddha was carried, surrounded by incense. It was also customary to have your picture taken at the casket. I was asked to be involved in this ritual. "I would be honored," I said to Bian. "Thank you so much for including me." These pictures could then be sent back to the village in Vietnam for those family members who could not attend the funeral. This custom was not entirely foreign to me. Growing up as a little girl in an Italian family, I can remember this being done. Wakes at that time were often held in someone's living room. At the time, I remember thinking, "This seems kind of strange. I wonder why they are taking pictures of a dead person?" My childhood curiosity was not in keeping with my understanding of my nationality or religion at the time. My mother explained to me that they would be sent back to Italy to the extended family members who could not come to the funeral. I felt a little better about it after hearing that. And this is what I was witnessing now as an adult with these people who were of the Buddhist religion.

I was unable to remain for the entire ceremony. Tuyet was cremated and her ashes would be taken by a family member to be buried at the temple in Vietnam where she worshipped as a young girl. This was one of the family's promises that were kept out of great respect for their mother. It was their duty and honor to fulfill her final request. I can still picture her smile the day that we first discussed this. She wanted to be reunited with her roots and she knew her final wish would be fulfilled.

I learned a great deal about other cultures and customs from this family. One universal theme that is always present is that of the great love family members have for their loved one. It is very personal and based on what they were taught as children. It is important that the religious beliefs be followed. The solemness and respect shown to Tuyet is one thing I will never forget. I learned that sometimes it is the unspoken words that heal us. I saw the power of silence and personal restraint at the bedside of the deceased. I witnessed the importance of kept promises which can bring so much peace to the dying person. For all this I am grateful. Thank you to Tuyet and her family.

Tell Her My Words

I watched her eyes as the family spoke
To tell her of my words
She listened most attentively
And took a turn with hers

I learned of a far-off country
Where she had spent her youth
Then travel to this foreign place
Which now would be her truth

I marveled at her strength and grace
As pain would surely come
But it would not affect her now
She chose to fight and won

Her final sun had come to set, and it was time
For her to travel home
With great celebration and respect
They led her to the throne

I watched in pure amazement
As the room was filled with sounds
Different from the other times
I'd watch as families frowned

Yes, it was a joyous time
For this is the world she lived in
And she would die in this same way
Thanking Buddha for all she had been given

ALLISON

The next visit I will share is another child. She was the first and only child of a young couple. Her father, Michael, was a college student who played football. Mom, Michelle, was a senior in high school, looking forward to furthering her education. She was a petite young woman whose eyes always seem to be wandering somewhere else. I would learn in the next few weeks, that her small stature was a direct contrast to her strength. She knew she wanted to attend college. Like a lot of young people her age, she was not sure of her exact major. Having two daughters myself, I identified with her enthusiasm and her struggle.

"I can imagine all the questions that must be crowding your head at this time, Michelle. You thought of your life going a certain way, not knowing that things would change so much."

She stood silent for a few moments, and then said, "Some days I wake up and I cannot believe that all of this has happened to me. I try to talk to Michael about it, but I don't want to get him upset. I know from my faith that everything happens for a reason. Sometimes it's just so hard to see that." The plan changed almost 16 months ago, when Allison was born. Life sometimes causes circumstances to go in a direction we never expect. This was certainly the case with the birth of Allison. She was welcomed with an overwhelming love into a large Irish Catholic family. They were more than ready to help care for this new little one, whatever that would mean. Over the next few months, I would see repeatedly how this family rallied around Michael and Michelle to help care for their precious child.

As far as their own families were concerned, Michelle was the middle child and had two sisters. One was still in high school, and the other had gone on to college. She and her younger sibling were especially close. She would often visit after school to talk with Michelle, and, of course, to hold her precious little niece. Michelle's face would light up when she would talk about these times. They were definitely a ray of sunshine in her day. "I love when Becky comes over. We talk about stuff we did together as kids. We laugh a lot. And that's good." Her older sister would visit from college whenever she could. She was kept updated through phone calls and letters and pictures of Allison. Her parents lived about three miles away. Her mother, Jackie, did not work outside the home, so she was available to come almost every day. Like most moms, she made delicious meals and tried to keep Michael and Michelle well fed. I made it a point to sit down with her and have a "mother to mother, talk," and she was eager to do so.

"I have two young daughters myself, Jackie. I hope that I would be as half as strong as you are in dealing with this heartache that you are witnessing. Allison is a beautiful child. Looking at her, you would hardly know she is sick." She agreed. "Yes, that's the thing. She really does not look sick. If it weren't for that feeding tube in her nose, she would look like any normal toddler. I feel so helpless, especially when I see Michelle and Michael so upset. I tell them all the time that they are great parents. The way they take care of their little girl is so loving." We talked for a while. Jackie shared some stories of Michelle as a little girl and she brought out some pictures to show me how much Alison looked like her mother. It was a brief moment of laughter and some smiles. "Michelle is taking lots of pictures of Allison," she told me. I said that was great! This way she would have a lot of memories to look at in the coming days and weeks.

Michelle's father was a postal carrier. From the stories Jackie shared, I could see he had developed a close relationship with Michael. The two of them would get together to talk, watch football and do other guy stuff. This was very comforting to her, especially since they had no sons. Our social worker had made plans to meet with Michelle's dad on the weekend when he had the time to sit down with her. Michael had three siblings: two brothers and a sister. He was the youngest in the family. He described their relationship as close.

"I could call any of them and they would be there for me. It's a great outlet to get out and throw the football around with my brothers. And of course, my sister dotes on me and does her girl thing." A big smile crossed his face. "My parents are great too. My dad is a construction worker and has long hours. But no matter how late it gets, he'll always come over to check on Michelle and me and Allison. My mom will call Michelle to find out when she can come over to give her a break. She loves her time with Allison. She is a great baker, and her cookies are super!" I could see the support of Michael's family meant a lot to him. Everyone seemed to have their own role, and they were all superstars as far as he was concerned. "You are lucky to have all these people helping and looking out for you, Michelle, and Allison. It's a really nice thing to see." He nodded in agreement and smiled.

Allison was born with a condition that did not allow her to take in food orally. She was sent home from the hospital with a feeding tube. The goal was to allow her to receive nutrition as long as possible. It was a fact that her disease would eventually cause her esophagus to occlude (block). Also, there was a high likelihood that tumors would form in her stomach. Regardless of how the disease process would present itself, the result was the same. A very poor prognosis for this little girl and a very difficult realization for this young family to take on. Seeing Michael and Michelle living with this realization showed me repeatedly how strong these two were.

Although the number of children we see in hospice is not a large percentage of our total census, these little ones have a monumental effect on the team. As with any new case, each person on the team brings their own life experiences and emotions to the table. We are keenly aware that caring for a dying child needs a special type of approach. Add to that the needs of the parents and extended family. You quickly realize these are the cases that will tug at your heartstrings like no other. The support of the teammates is especially important as emotions can run high. The question often surfaces, "How can we keep each other grounded?" These types of cases call on each of us to be there to support each other in a special way. Some members might have children around the age of a patient. Some might have a questioning of their faith or spiritual beliefs. I know at times I did. "What is God's plan for this little one and her parents? Do I have the strength to cope as these two young parents are doing?" I was sad and angry at the same time. I knew I had to call upon my professionalism and expertise to give this family the best care, which is what they deserved. I called another hospice nurse who was my mentor when I first took on this role. It was great to talk with someone who knew exactly where I was coming from. It's not that she gave me advice that I had not heard before, it was that she listened and validated my feelings. In a way, the hospice nurse had become a client. Sometimes you must remember what you have told your families and realize that it may apply to you as well. Whatever the circumstance may be, the importance of team members' support of each other came into play now more than ever.

I made the call to arrange my initial visit. Consents needed to be signed. That officially began Allison's hospice care. The first meeting with these young parents was emotional for everyone at the table. They had asked if the grandparents could be included, as they were a large part of Allison's life and a huge support to them.

"I think that's a great idea. It's important for everyone involved in her care to understand how hospice will be helping her and all of you."

They listened attentively and asked pertinent questions. "Can you get medicine for Allison, so she won't suffer?" Michelle's mother asked.

I answered her in this way, "I will work closely with her doctor to make sure she has little or no pain. Once the request is made, medicine can get here to the house very quickly. If need be, we can even get it from a local pharmacy and have it here, usually within an hour. Everyone on the hospice team is also dedicated to this outcome for your granddaughter."

"Will there be a lot of people coming into the house?" Michelle asked.

I shared with her the importance of her and Michael having their own alone time with Allison. I had a feeling this was on Michael's mind as well.

"You will always know who is coming and what time their visits are planned. If it's not a good time for you, just let us know. We can always reschedule our visits to better suit your needs." I told them I would probably visit daily for a few days to be sure that the family understood what needed to be done for Allison's care. I then would discuss with them what the schedule would look like going forward. Everyone agreed that was a good idea. Any type of visiting nursing should come with the preconceived fact that you are a guest in this person's home. You may be the medical expert, but this is a person they love and cherish. They look to you for advice and comfort.

Allison was a beautiful, happy little girl. Her demeanor camouflaged her underlying illness and poor prognosis. As the hospice nurse my visits included assessing her vital signs and comfort level. How were the tube feedings going? Did her mother understand the signs and symptoms which needed to be reported to the hospice team? Michelle indicated that things were going well, and she felt very comfortable with the procedure.

"Does Alison seem to be tolerating the feedings? Is there anything you observe that makes you think she's uncomfortable with them?" I asked.

"Well, sometimes she fusses when I first connect the tube to the feeding bag. I think that's because she doesn't like to lie still. She'd rather just keep playing." We both agreed that that seemed like a reasonable reaction for a little child such as Allison. I asked her to please let me know if at any time that had changed.

Allison's father attended class for most of the day. His physical demeanor was a stark contrast to the emotional trials he was facing. Michael was a strong young man. It was difficult for him to express his feelings. We made it clear the hospice team was there for him, whatever that might mean. He was able to help in the late afternoon and evenings, giving Michelle some much needed rest. He had also learned how to give the feedings and what to look for at this time. He said he really didn't have any questions, but he would call me if he did.

Grandparents also lent support and were a frequent presence in the home. They would bring meals and offer Michael and Michelle some respite. They were trying to bring some type of normalcy into this very abnormal situation. Their visits also allowed Michael and Michelle some alone time together. Yes, they were two very caring parents, and they were also a young couple who needed that type of time.

So how do you support a young couple that is facing the certain death of their child? In this case, it began with some practical teaching so that Allison could be cared for at home. This meant learning to change the nasogastric tube should that be needed in an emergency. This was Allison's means of receiving a special formula which contained vitamins and nutrients. It enters through the nose and passes into the stomach. I am always amazed by how non-medical family members can learn the treatments necessary for their loved one's care. There is never a question or any hesitancy that certain modalities be learned. The power of love takes over. Most treatments are performed by the nurse, however, if there would be an extended delay for some reason, families may be taught to step in.

"You really understand about Allison's feeding tube. I can tell just by watching you," I told her. "Remember, if you ever need to review any of the treatment, just call me. I may be able to talk you through it on the phone or I will make a visit if needed."

Michelle seemed relieved at this news. "Thanks, Linda. That's really good to know. It makes me feel a lot better about doing this for Allison. It kind of eases my mind that if I had a question, I could get somebody on the phone right away."

I nodded and explained to her that I would also review this with Michael on one of my later visits when he was home from class.

Michelle thought that was a great idea. "I think Mike's a little more nervous than I am about the tube. I mean, he's willing to do it and he does a good job, but I think talking to you about it would make him feel a lot better." I promised to call Mike and set up that visit.

I wanted to know how Michelle was coping with all this at her young age. What experience did she have to draw from? I asked her. "Michelle, it can't be easy caring for your child who's so ill. How do you do it?"

She didn't hesitate. "Well, she is my daughter and God brought her to me. I love taking care of her for as long as I have her. I get sad a lot and cry at night when nobody's around.

But then I see her smiling face and she's jumping up and down in the crib and all that goes away. So, I guess it's Allison that keeps me going."

To me, this was such a cruel irony. Here was a little girl, whose illness is causing such sadness because it will take her away soon. But she is the same little girl whose smile lights up her mother's life.

"Allison is a special little girl, Michelle, and you are a special mom." I reminded her that the team was there to support her. The fact that she was crying at night was not an unusual thing to hear. In times of great stress, people tend to do whatever is needed for their loved one. When nighttime finally comes, they take a deep breath, try to relax, and allow themselves to cry. I asked her about friends that she might have. "Have you had any visitors lately? Do your friends from school have a chance to come over and spend some time with you?"

She said she did have a few good friends that would either call or come over to visit. These were times she enjoyed, even though they did not happen very often. "My main concern is Allison. She's the one that needs me now. There'll be plenty of time for friends later." Her voice trailed off. I could see the dedication she felt to take care of her child. It was the most important thing in her life.

What did the support system for this young couple look like? The entire family had strong ties to the Catholic Church they attended. Their religion was clearly a support to them. I had to wonder. Did it also bring a certain amount of guilt? Do they feel they are being punished for something? These are questions that may come up and are not easily answered. It is not unusual for our hospital chaplain to collaborate with the priests, rabbi or minister already supporting our families.

Their priest was able to share valuable history of these young parents. Likewise, our chaplain was a teacher and support person specializing in hospice care. These two worked very well together to offer the best possible spiritual support. Many questions are raised regarding faith in a situation such as this one, involving a young child. Many tough questions are posed. Why did this happen to our child? Michael and Michelle did not articulate this exactly. Somehow, I knew some of these questions must have been haunting them. Could this have been prevented somehow? Was there something that they did as parents? Did they miss something? Could this illness have been prevented?

The social worker is a valuable part of the support phase. Janet was assigned to this case. She shared her insights at our team meeting. "Although this is a young couple, I can tell they are dedicated to caring for their child. They've been dating for almost two years. They hinted this was turning into a meaningful relationship. They said they had discussed marriage but not as anything that would happen soon. Michael was still in college and Michelle not quite finished with high school. They were forthright about feeling afraid. What was going to happen next with Allison? How much longer were they going to have her? Would they know what to do if she was in pain?

All these concerns were very much what our team would expect in a situation such as this. Janet expressed that she felt she was able to allay a portion of their fears. She had a son about the same age as Allison. She related to Michelle as a young mother. She would be with them to offer insight during these difficult conversations. We also reminded Janet that if she needed any support from the team, she only needed to ask. If areas involving some practical stuff would come up, Janet could also assist in that. Things like insurance coverage, family respite, and funeral arrangements sometimes need clarification.

I scheduled an early evening visit to meet with Michael one day. "How has it been going for you, Michael? It must be tough keeping a full schedule of class just now. I bet it's hard to concentrate." I was hoping he would see this as an opportunity to share his feelings with me.

"Well, everybody at school has been really good. I've been able to leave class early on days when I need to. That gives me more time to come home to see Allison and to help Michelle, I know how tired she gets. And we both are so worried about Allison."

This is the first time I noticed that Michael was near tears. Listening to him speak, my heart was breaking for him. "Is there anything I can do to help you, Michael? Do you have any questions I can answer right now?" There probably were a million questions and there probably wasn't anything I could really do. But I asked anyway.

He shared with me that he wanted to be sure he was doing everything right as he took care of Allison, especially regarding the feeding tube. "I would never want to hurt her or make her feel any kind of pain. I'm pretty sure I'm doing

85

everything right. Michelle watches me and says I'm doing a decent job."

I had no doubt he was doing the best job anyone could. "Yes, Michelle says you are a great dad and a great nurse to Allison." That second remark made us chuckle.

It was hard for him to articulate his feelings. The one thing he was able to say to me was this. "I just wish she didn't have to die. Every day I wake up and wonder if it's going to be the day she will leave us. People ask me if I'm mad at God, and I guess sometimes I am. I talk to my priest, and he helps me understand some things. But it still doesn't change anything." He started to cry, and I cried right along with him. This was one of those times when the best gift was silence. We both stood in the moment. I then said to him. "Michael. I cannot even imagine how you feel. Please know that I am here to help you, whatever that means." I touched his arm. He nodded his head and said simply, "Thank you."

It's a moment I will never forget.

I was working the day that Allison died. It was in the middle of the afternoon when I received a call from our social worker, Janet, who was already at the home. As I walked into the house, my mind started to race as it usually did at a time like this. I began to pray for guidance. I prayed for help to know what words to say to help these two young people. They had lost their precious angel. This little one who came into their lives such a brief time ago and now was leaving. They cherished every moment with her. How could words ever be enough?

Somehow the words came, surrounded by hugs and

tears. Michael answered the door, so he was the first person I saw. "Michael, I am so sorry. Allison was such a beautiful little child. I am so sorry." He was crying, more like sobbing. To see this tall, strong young man falling apart before my very eyes was just so sad. Michelle was standing in the corner of the room being hugged by her mother. She looked so small. I believe she was in shock. I went over to her and hugged her for what seemed like a long time. I offered her my condolences, as I had done with Michael.

I gently removed the feeding tube and did a short physical assessment. I looked down to see the face of an angel, free of that tube and free from any illness.

I stayed at the house until the funeral director arrived. By this time various family members had also come. Since this was a small child, there was no need for the traditional hearse. I looked outside to see a black station wagon. When it was time for Allison to be carried out of the house, Michael scooped her up with Michelle at his side. They walked down the sidewalk to the waiting car. Although it was no more than ten feet, the walk seemed endless. He was crying with a profound sadness that would break your heart. Michelle was hanging on his arm. She was extremely weak and almost fell. The undertaker opened the back of the station wagon to reveal a small black box. It was very plain and had a dull finish. I could not believe my eyes. Did I really have to lay Allison in this awful box? I felt my face freezing with an expression of horror. I hoped no one else could see it. This awful box. I felt that this was not befitting of our little angel. I could feel myself becoming very upset. I prayed for strength. The social worker motioned that I should take Allison from Michael's arms. I imagine that she thought he may not be able to let her go. He resisted at first. Just before she was given to me, these young parents each kissed her on one cheek. It would be the last time they would be seeing her. Then Michelle took his arm, as they looked at each other. I gently took Allison from him. As I turned back toward the car, my eyes were stunned and surprised. That black box was open to reveal a small, beautiful resting place for Allison. It was made of white satin and lace with a small pillow for Allison to rest her head. I carefully put her down, thinking how small and innocent she was. I will never forget how peaceful and beautiful she looked. At this moment, she was perfect. Janet and I guided the parents back toward the house before the lid was closed. It would be better if they could remember their final picture of Alison as this special little girl lying in a bed of satin and lace.

I called the family the next day to see how they were coping and was there anything that they needed. Mom was going through some pictures. She shared that although Alison was not here on earth very long, she touched a lot of people's lives. She offered thanks to the hospice team. I thanked her in return for allowing us to walk with her and her family on this very special journey. This was a time of much gratitude for me as her hospice nurse. Like everyone I have had the honor of caring for, I was given many gifts by this little girl. Somehow Allison, when I look up at the sky and see those white fluffy clouds, I will think of you and your smile and how much you brought to all of us. This is a priceless gift which lifts me up on many occasions. I am often asked how does a person face so much sadness every day and continue to care for the next patient? The truth is the gifts given by every hospice patient and their families are gifts of faith and love. They show me that I can go on despite witnessing great losses. With this knowledge, my soul is lifted, and I am renewed. And I can continue.

After such a difficult case as this, the hospice team will meet to discuss how each of us is doing. It is important that we support each other as feelings come to surface. We all need to be honest about how the case has affected us. It might be described as a type of emotional decompression. I remember one of my first supervisors explaining it. After a difficult case, our emotional gas tank is nearing empty. You must find a way of filling it up before you can go on to another patient. Leaning on the team is a sure way to do this. With me personally, I am fortunate to have the support of two, understanding daughters, Jenna and Alissa, who are both in the "helping professions." This brings an important dimension to their ability to help me process my own sadness. I know I can count on them to be my safe place to fall, should that be what I need. My faith sustains me as well. My final prayer with any case is to thank God for his continuing support and strength. In this way, I can be spiritually renewed. I can go on and continue to do the work that I so love. And I feel very fortunate.

This Child

Come to me Lord as I care
for this child
Give me the gift to be
strong
Whisper the words that help
me to speak
With a wisdom that cannot
be wrong

Bless my hands to minister
in your name
and give them the care they
all need
To help ease their pain and help heal
their wounds for surely you have
planted the seed

And then for the families who need
So much faith
To travel this road and endure
We know this time may be full
of great doubt and the need for
a love that is sure

Give them the strength to
persevere
As they sadly prepare their farewell
To these small angels
you will shortly receive
Forever in heaven to dwell

MARIE

This chapter is especially emotional for me to write. Marie was my sister-in-law, but I always considered her my sister. I had been married to her brother, and I remained in close contact with her and her family even after our separation. Her children gave permission for the first names of the family to be used. Thank you to Sylvia, RoseAnn, John, Stephen and MaryBeth. I shared many holidays and family events with this loving group of people. I believe my closeness to Marie stemmed from the fact that our philosophies on motherhood were very closely aligned. I was not her hospice nurse in an official capacity, however I assisted with care decisions and supported the family whenever called to do so. As I was a part of this family for many years, we had built a level of trust that we all knew we could count on.

Marie's life had always been dedicated to the care of her children and extended family members. During the time she was still employed, Marie worked in the office of a local elementary school. She would share stories of the children she had come to know. It was not unlike her to bring in small gifts to these little ones. She was the perfect person for this type of job. She was the person all the nieces and nephews would go to for advice or a listening ear. She truly had a gift. Even in her days of increasing illness, her personality showed through. She was always available for others.

"Mom seems to be getting tired much more easily these days," Sylvia reported. "I really think she could use some help, at least a few days a week."

I did not respond immediately. Although I was interested in helping her, through the years I had always been there for Marie as a family member. This seemed more official, more like a job, and that was strange to me.

"Well, Sylvia," I said, "I could do it now that I'm retired. I have the time."

She thought it was a good idea. "Let's see what Mom says. She's never been one to accept help, but I think she might from you."

So, it was decided that we would meet with Marie at her house in the next few days. Marie was open to the idea, so the three of us sat down at the kitchen table. "Mom. What do you think about Linda coming in to help you a few days a week? You were saying how you were feeling so tired." Sylvia posed the question, and Marie quickly answered. "Oh, Linda, would you want to do that?" She sounded hopeful and enthusiastic.

"Well, of course, Marie. You know, you are like my sister, and I would be so glad to help you." She took my hand, and a big smile came to her face. "Oh, this will be so nice." We discussed a few details to get things started. "Next week is good for me, Marie. How about I come on Tuesdays and Fridays? Is 8 to 12 good for you?"

She agreed that it was perfect. And so, I began my visits as planned. Mitch Albom, the famous author, had "Tuesdays with Morrie." I would have Tuesdays and Fridays with Marie. It would prove to be a very special time for both of us.

Marie and I decided I would help her with personal care and some household tasks. She was a very thin, frail woman, whose gait was affected by a severe spinal condition that she had for many years. She had a cane that she used to steady herself. It was not something she enjoyed using, and she kept, accidentally on purpose, misplacing it. I found myself asking her at least five times a day, "Marie, where is your cane?" She would laugh, and we would both start hunting to find it. We decided it would be better if we had a few canes placed in various rooms, so one would always be available when she needed it. "This way you won't have to be yelling at me all the time, Linda," she said with a sheepish grin. She never complained or mentioned it as a reason for her not being able to do the things she wanted to. We worked like a well-oiled machine.

Each visit started at eight AM with Marie greeting me at that front door. I could smell the coffee brewing. She would pour us each a cup as we took our positions at the kitchen table. So many important conversations have been held there.

"How have you been feeling, Marie? Are you sleeping, okay?"

She reported that sleep was not a problem. As far as pain, I am certain, Marie suffered with it every day. Her severe arthritis and spinal condition were two of the major causes. Every time I questioned her about it, her answer was usually the same. "Oh, it's not that bad. A lot of people have it worse than me." And that is exactly how she felt.

We discussed how things were going since she had stopped smoking about a month ago. This was a huge undertaking, as she had been smoking since she was a teenager. The nicotine patch was effective. I assisted Marie with her medication and changed the patch as ordered. Marie's son-in-law Victor had erected several bird feeders in the backyard. I would say he was the official family handyman. "Oh, that

Victor, he is something else. Anything I need, I just mention it and he's there the next day to fix it. I don't know what I would do without him." Victor was Sylvia's husband. He truly cared about his mother-in-law and was there for her at a moment's notice. The prime example was the bird feeders in the backyard, which he had erected. He knew Marie's love of birds and that this view from her kitchen table was one she really enjoyed. The view from the window was a virtual aviary dance. And oh, those squirrels! We witnessed how they would get their share of the seeds and other delights intended for the birds. In true Marie fashion, she lamented," Well, I guess they have to eat too." These conversations would be a large part of the many sweet memories I have of Marie and me.

Marie had five wonderful children. The youngest of the five was Marie's daughter, Mary Beth. She lived over an hour away and had two small children. Marie was introduced to the idea of "Facetiming" from Mary Beth and her little ones. They may not have been able to visit every weekend, but they certainly visited by phone a few times a week. "Oh, I just love seeing their smiles! I am so lucky to have these little ones around, just like all my other grandchildren."

Mary Beth was a toddler when her father died. I remember one conversation I had with her. "I really don't remember my dad, and no one has really told me much about him. It's something that I've always wondered about." I understood her need for information and shared what I could about this loving father. My hope was that this gave Mary Beth some peace. I would often hear the story of thanks told by Marie. It was regarding the fact that I opened my home to the mourners after Walter, her husband's funeral. My mother was at my house doing the cooking with Mary Beth as her able assistant. To this day, Mary Beth often speaks of my mother as a second grandmother. The feeling of great affection was mutual. When a hospice patient has a large family, there is a particular need to realize the individuality of each as they view end of life care and death. Each of the siblings had their own way of helping Marie as her needs changed. I was in close contact with each one as questions arose. Being the oldest, Sylvia had a way of directing her siblings as questions came up. She would often arrange a group phone call, so all of us could hear the same thing at one time. We also had a group text which made it easy to share concerns. John did not live close by but would stop frequently with groceries and to help with the bills. One of his favorite things to bring his mother was ice cream. If it were up to him, she would never run out.

"John, how much ice cream do you think I can eat?"she would tease him.

"Well, Mom, you never know what kind you might like, so I brought you a few choices."

Roseanne worked during the day at a daycare center. If Marie ever needed anything, she would be there right after her work was done. Her talent with children and love for them is one thing she inherited from her mother.

"Roseanne. You've got to slow down and get some rest," Marie would caution.

"Yes. Mother, I know," Roseanne would tease.

Along with the Tuesday card game, Marie also looked forward to her Saturday mornings. That's when her other son,

Stephen, would stop in for coffee and a lot of great conversation. You can be sure there were some wild stories and lots of laughter going on in that kitchen on those days. If I had to choose a title for Stephen, it would be family comedian.

"Yes, Stephen always makes me laugh. I'm always glad when Saturday comes around because I know I'll be seeing him," Marie would say.

I can honestly say that Marie's family embraced the hospice philosophy like no other family with whom I have had the pleasure of working. At one of our family meetings, I commented, "I want everybody to remember that you can call me anytime, day or night. If you have a question or are worried about something, maybe I can help. You know how close I've always been to your mom. There isn't anything I wouldn't do for her or any of you." I looked up to see some tear-stained faces. This was just so difficult for everyone, including me. I was a professional nurse, but I was also a family member. This is a struggle I have faced many times in my life. Having the knowledge to give information to your family, but also needing to be able to express yourself as just a person.

Marie struggled to keep a sense of normalcy. One of her greatest joys were the visits, calls and drawings from her grandchildren and great grandchildren. Not even the likes of a great painting could compete with the artwork of these little ones. Marie's entire refrigerator was covered with photos of each of them. "I just love all these pictures and drawings I get. It's like getting a visit from each of the kids when I look at them." I agreed. There's nothing sweeter than receiving something in the mail and knowing the love that was put into it.

Another thing that Marie enjoyed were the Tuesday night card games. She would start the preparation early in the day. The table in the spare room was set with the cards, napkins, paper plates, sugar, and sweetener. Of course, the coffee would be brewed closer to the time that everyone would arrive.

"I think you have everything ready, Marie. Is this a high stakes game or just a friendly competition?" I laughed as I posed that question to her.

"We don't usually lose any money here, but you never know." She smiled, and we both knew that this was going to be a good night for her. Tuesday evenings always were.

As with all hospice patients, Marie's needs changed with respect to her ability to perform self-care and keep a sense of normalcy. Her condition took a decided turn one day as her oxygen level was seriously low. Her daughter Sylvia sensed that something was wrong during a phone conversation. She went to her mother's home and found her to be very confused. Her pulse oxygen level showed a dangerous level of 66. A normal level should be in the 90s. It was clear that Marie needed swift medical intervention. This would be the day that Marie was admitted to the hospital. This is the day everything changed. I immediately went to the hospital, and it did not take long for the whole family to be assembled there.

The course of Marie's illness changed steadily after this hospitalization. Her heart was failing which led to continued respiratory difficulties. Onset of confusion is typical with a low pulse oxygen level. It may be difficult for families who communicate with their loved ones due to the onset of hypoxia which is a decreased oxygen level to the brain. The wonderful conversations Marie always enjoyed with her children were not possible at this time. Any oxygen her body would produce would first be used to maintain function of her vital organs. This is how the brain works to keep these systems going.

Restlessness and anxiety related to this lack of oxygen are common symptoms. The doctor would order specific medications to help control these symptoms. It is often helpful to have familiar faces present when a person is experiencing them. This need was easily met by everyone in the family. I posed this question, "I think it's a good idea if we all sit down and get a schedule together. This way we will know who's coming and what time slots still need to be filled? I will be glad to coordinate this if that's okay with everybody."

The decision was unanimous that we would all do this. We took turns staying with Marie, helping to calm her during episodes of anxiety.

I must share an interesting story that happened one night at the hospital. Marie was especially confused. She was asking to go home and wanted a cigarette. It was around 2:00 o'clock in the morning and I happened to be there with her. "Marie, you are in the hospital. You can't go home right now because you still need some help. There is no smoking here. If the nurse lets you smoke, she will get into a lot of trouble. I know you would not want that." Appealing to her sense of compassion did not work. She became visibly annoyed with me. "Linda, of all people, I cannot believe you are turning against me." I felt as if I was betraying my sister. Of course, I knew what was best for her. I called for the nurse to see if there was any suggestion she might have to help Marie. She had an idea which seemed strange at the time but proved to be very successful. She took an ordinary drinking straw and cut it in half. "Here, Marie, here's your cigarette." She handed the straw to Marie who took it and started to puff on it as if it were a real cigarette. I was amazed! The nurse shared she had tried this with another patient in the past and it had worked also. I guess the idea of having something in her hand, somehow made her brain think she was smoking a real cigarette. She started to calm down.

"Marie, how about if I get us a cup coffee and we can sit and talk like we always do?"

She agreed and sat down on the side of her bed. I hoped she would be getting tired soon and be able to get some much needed rest. I encouraged her to get in bed. I put on the television. I sat close by on the recliner and reassured her that I would be there all night. I said my nightly prayers, and she fell asleep. I shared this incident with our family handyman, Victor, who researched the actual size of a real cigarette. He discovered it is the size of half of a McDonald's straw. So of course, he obtained a supply to have ready for when Marie got home. I will tell you, she continued to use them, and they were a godsend. You can always count on the inventive talent of a clever nurse.

The time frame I am speaking of now included the Christmas holiday and days leading up to it. The special meaning of Christmas to Marie's family cannot be adequately described. She had hosted a Christmas Eve gathering at her home for as long as I can remember. Her home was literally bursting at the seams with family and close friends who would stop in for some Christmas cheer. And there was plenty of it to be had at that home. The Christmas tree stood by the front window with an untold number of gifts pouring out on the floor. There was a buffet on the kitchen table, ready for all to share. Marie was famous for her homemade eggnog topped with fresh whipped cream. I had started a tradition many years ago of bringing a homemade cheese ball and my famous fudge. What you need to know about the fudge is that it was for Marie only. She would take it from me and immediately hide it in the back of the refrigerator. "I can't wait to start eating my fudge." We hugged each other, knowing this would be a great night. But this year would be different. Without Marie, it just wouldn't be the same. Sylvia and Victor hosted the party at their home. Everyone gathered, but it was not the usual celebration. Everyone involved tried to keep some semblance of a Christmas spirit for the sake of the small children who still hoped for Santa to visit.

Marie's final months were spent in a lovely, assisted living in the next town from where she lived. It reflected the Moravian influence which permeates this part of the city. The outside gave the feeling of a well-kept mansion. It had a large porch lined with rocking chairs. "This is great. I'll be able to sit outside. During the warm weather," Marie commented. As I looked around, I could feel each of us giving a collective sigh. Large hanging baskets of flowers adorned the edges. I was familiar with this building as I had seen hospice patients here during my time as a field nurse. I remembered it as a positive experience. When you entered this dwelling, it was like stepping back in time. Antique furniture and lamps adorned the sitting room. Marie had a beautiful room on the first floor. There was also a rocking chair in her room. She shared that room with a very pleasant woman, Elizabeth. They shared the bathroom as well. There were fresh flowers in a vase and a beautiful painting on the wall. Looking around, you could tell this was a comfortable room. As the family quickly learned, the care here was exemplary. Each staff member possessed a kindness and level of professionalism that reassured us that Marie was in a loving place. Staff worked well with hospice members who visited Marie frequently. I arranged to be in Marie's room when her hospice nurse came for one of her assessment visits. She was happy to meet me here and gave me a clinical update. Marie's condition was declining daily. We discussed medication she had available, especially for her shortness of breath. The staff made it clear that she would be on continuous oxygen. They would be sure Marie's oxygen was with her when she went to sit on the front porch. And that's exactly what they did, each and every time. Sylvia was known to treat the staff with some delicious gifts, such as her homemade cream of spinach soup. You might say this was a family specialty. Meals were shared in a quaint dining room. It was as if you were sitting down at a family table. "The food is delicious," Marie reported. "and everybody is really nice. No matter what I ask for, they will always try to get it for me." We all agreed things were going very well here.

A small elevator was available to take residents to the second floor. Medications were given by a health aide who had special training in medication administration. A few times I had occasion to call the staff to clarify orders or ask questions regarding Marie's care. They always answered me in a timely manner. It made me feel secure knowing that my sister was being cared for by this wonderful group of people. The entire environment exuded a calmness that made everyone feel safe.

I remember the night my sister Marie died. Her breathing had changed drastically. Sylvia was already with her mother. She called the other family members. Oxygen and the administration of liquid morphine helped her to be more comfortable. The hospice nurse was notified so that she could be in touch with the doctor to obtain any necessary medication changes. One by one, each of her five children arrived with their spouses and Marie's grandchildren and great grandchildren. Her brother Jim and his wife also came. Marie had all the people she dearly loved at her bedside. I feel blessed to be named among these along with my two daughters, Jenna my oldest, and Alissa Marie, named for Marie, her aunt and godmother. I spoke to the staff about my concern for her roommate. The aide spoke with Elizabeth, who asked if she could please remain in the room. We all agreed that if that's what she wanted to do, she would be welcome. She and Marie had become fast friends during her short stay there.

"Thank you, Elizabeth. Please let me know if there's anything I can get you or if you change your mind about staying in the room. There is an empty bed you can use down the hall." She nodded and thanked me.

We took turns at each side of the bed holding Marie's hands. Every person did whatever they felt comfortable doing. Speaking to her or just being present. We in hospice encourage loved ones to speak if they wish. Although patients usually cannot respond, we are certain they can hear the words that are being spoken to them. It is a very special and personal time. We were all very respectful of each other's wishes. We allowed each person to do whatever they felt comfortable doing at this most special time.

The angels came for Marie as everyone was gathering around her bed. Yes, the tears flowed but there was also a sense of relief. Being a family of faith, we knew Marie was in a good place. We asked if the family could give us some privacy. Sylvia and I bathed Marie. It was a final gift and our way of honoring her. I wondered, how many baths she had given in her lifetime? She was a mother, grandmother, sister, and friend. She was loved by everyone whose life she touched. She would be dearly missed. One by one, we each came back to the room. Some of us held Marie's hand, some of us spoke to her, others just sat quietly. Each one expressing themselves, as they needed to say goodbye to this wonderful person.

My gift from Marie was witnessing the great power of a mother's love. It was present in every aspect of her life. Who will your grandchildren and nieces and nephews come to now, as they seek a listening ear? Who will I sit with and have that great cup of coffee that we shared so many times? Anyone who met her knew there was something so special about this woman. Her legacy is that she showed us the great importance of loving one another for exactly who we are. I thank you my sister from the bottom of my heart. I will think of you whenever I see a bird in a birdhouse, whenever I see a squirrel running up a tree, whenever I smell a pot of fresh coffee brewing. These things and so much more will be the wonderful memories I will keep in my heart. You will be sorely missed.

Since I was related to Marie, you might imagine bereavement follow up was very different. I spoke frequently with my nieces and nephews in the days and weeks following her death. We told stories, we laughed, and we cried. But the one thing that has never changed is the great love we have for each other as members of a wonderful family. It was Marie's influence and strong sense of family that guided us. I feel fortunate to be part of this remarkable family. I have said thank you to God many times.

I Called Her My Sister

Joined by the heart, with much love to share
I called her my sister, the bond here was clear

We knew we were special as each day went by
It seemed our connection reached up to the sky

I could smell the coffee brewing as she came to the door
And so it began, conversation and so much more

I'd go twice a week and offer whatever care was needed
I'd listen to stories, some new, some repeated

The laughter we shared was more precious than gold
As each day flew by, more stories were told

We were not joined by blood, but something more real
The power of knowing exactly what the other could feel

Time went by quickly, each day was a prize
Our hearts told us first
Things our minds would come to realize

You were here until you were no more
You left me, my sister, but this I know for sure
All the laughter and tears
Came from the truest of love that time can endure

And when I tell my stories of all those times with you
I will say. "Oh yes, she was my family. My sister tried and true."

PRACTICAL INFORMATION

A Nurse in the Family

Among the many roles I play as a hospice nurse, guide and educator are important ones. As each case develops, necessary changes occur that cause the nurse-patient relationship to be born. It will forever change other relationships that have already been born in your life. As I was called to be the guide and educator for my own family, I could see my role as daughter swiftly changing, accompanied by a definite shift in my emotions. I was the one called upon to make decisions regarding medical care and treatment. I had the expertise, so it made sense that I did. And I did it willingly and with great love and compassion. But, I have to say there were days when the daughter in me was yearning to be heard. It was my own choosing that I kept her in the background. In times of crisis, my family was better served with my being the nurse. At least that's how I saw it at the time. But I wouldn't be honest if I didn't admit that it was an internal struggle. When people you love need your professional help, you give it willingly. But there is that big part of you that wants to give in to your personal feelings of grief and sadness.

I would like to share a few thoughts with the other nurses who may find themselves with these similar feelings. Be the nurse your family needs you to be when the medical world seems overwhelming to them. But do not forget, you are a member of the family first. These two roles are not mutually exclusive. It may be difficult to navigate wearing both hats at one time. We, as professionals, need to find a place where both can survive. At the end of the day, when you are away from the alarms and call bells, sit back and remember your own words about self-care. Let the dance you have been doing as a professional caregiver slow down from a tango to a waltz. Remember that the music you hear is your own composition, and it will change as your heart and mind tells it to. I believe that at the end of the day we all want a sense of peace. As nurses, we need to know the care that we have given was our best. As a family member, we cherish every person in our lives. We are grateful for the faith they have placed in us, and we continue to hold them in our hearts. This is the balance I wish for every nurse in every family.

Deciding on Hospice Care

If you or a family member has recently received the diagnosis of a terminal illness, hospice care may be appropriate at this time. Here is an easy guide as to how to proceed in obtaining this care:

1. It requires a "doctor's order" which means your physician refers you to the hospice organization of your choice. You can find these programs online. Your physician may also be helpful in this first step. It is important that the hospice you choose is Medicare and JCAHO (Joint Commission for Accreditation of Healthcare Organizations).This assures the highest standard of care and accessibility to all benefits included.

2. The hospice group will contact you to set up the initial evaluation. This includes signing of required consents and a physical assessment by the hospice nurse. The nurse will verify your insurance coverage. The details of services and equipment and medications covered are clearly defined.

3. All services and responsibilities of the Interdisciplinary team are explained by that discipline. These members include: the hospice nurse, home health aide if desired, the chaplain, and medical social worker. A volunteer is also available, as well as the various therapies if indicated—physical, occupational, speech, and complimentary therapies. The nurse will receive

the order from the physician to have the patient evaluated for these services. If appropriate for same, the individual therapist will secure ongoing orders as to the plan of care and goals of treatment.

4. Care given to a hospice patient centers around comfort and support. Each discipline has their own expertise in achieving these goals. The family is the unit of care. Their needs are addressed in each visit as the circumstances present themselves. The nurse formulates and controls the plan of care, a blueprint which outlines how needs will be met. A visit schedule is decided upon which is individualized to each patient.

Myths About Hospice Care

I'd like to address a few myths about hospice care:

1. Only persons with a diagnosis of terminal cancer are eligible for hospice care.

FACT: Any person whose physician certifies that he has an illness with a prognosis of six months or less is eligible for hospice care.

2. A person cannot be considered for hospice care if he does not know his diagnosis and/or his prognosis.

FACT: Although it is preferable for a person to be fully aware of his diagnosis and or prognosis, there are circumstances when this is not possible. One example would be in the case of Alzheimer's or other dementias. If a person is in a non-cognitive state, or if he's intellectually impaired and unable to make decisions for himself, are two examples. In these cases, the durable medical power of attorney would be consulted.

3. If a person lives alone, he is not eligible for hospice care.

FACT: The ideal circumstance would be for someone to have a caregiver living in their home at the time of the initial consent. That may not always be the case. The social worker would immediately start plans to decide on what course of action to take, as the patient becomes more dependent and would no longer be safe alone. This would include a financial assessment as to what the patient can afford. Some choices would be in home, help, assisted living, or skilled care.

4. A person is not eligible for hospice care if he or she resides in a facility such as an assisted living, a group home, or a skilled nursing home.

FACT: Wherever a person lives is the place where he or she can receive care. In the case of a skilled nursing facility, the hospice team would have to investigate to be sure the person was not admitted there for a skilled need. Under Medicare and other insurances, hospice itself is considered skilled care and therefore could not be initiated if another skill was already being charged. Wherever a person calls home is where they are entitled to receive hospice care. Programs such as the Medicare Hospice benefit and most major insurances recognize that not everyone is in the position to be cared for and die at home. There may be a lack of caregivers or the level of care they require is not conducive to a home setting. The staff at the facility continues to be the primary caregivers. The hospice team lends their expertise in areas such as pain management and symptom management. Emotional support is also extended to this group of people, as they often become like family to the patients they care for.

5. There is no high-tech care allowed while someone is on hospice.

FACT: The percentage of patients requiring some type of high-tech care is not the majority. If their plan of care would include something such as an analgesic pump for morphine or Dilaudid, it would be acceptable. Acceptance of these modalities is always decided on a case-by-case basis. The hospice medical director is the decision maker when there is a question of eligibility and coverage of these services. Other examples may be a feeding tube, Foley, catheter, or other types of external drains.

6. There is an age limit whereby a person cannot be signed on to hospice care, as with infants or children.

FACT: Eligibility for electing hospice care is driven by physician certification. It must be stated that the person has an end stage diagnosis with a poor prognosis of six months or less. Age does not play a factor in this consideration.

7. Hospice care includes the use of morphine and other opioids to help speed up the dying process.

FACT: This is a serious misconception about end-of-life care. All medications prescribed, such as morphine, are done under the direction of a physician. Good pain and symptom management tells us that the minimum dose of any medication should be used to achieve the maximum effect. The doses can be increased as a person's condition warrants. The hospice nurse or physician are both available to discuss this issue with families.

8. Any health care organization can notify a patient to start hospice care in their home.

FACT: The only way hospice care can be started is by the order of a physician. You should never be solicited by a phone call, or someone coming to your home to try and start hospice care. The regulations are very strict and governed by the federal and state governments. When inquiring about a hospice program, the family should be sure that the organizations they are speaking with are Medicare and JCAHO certified. Companies with these accreditations guarantee the highest quality of care. They have gone through grueling surveys and must maintain the latest medical standards in the home health and hospice fields. If this acronym is not part of their initial program information you would do well to choose another company.

9. Once a person signs on to hospice care, they must keep receiving care, even if for some reason they have changed their mind.

FACT: There are some circumstances whereby a person may decide to discontinue their hospice care. This is technically known as a revocation. One reason might be the discovery of a new cancer treatment which the person is electing to receive, or a person's condition has improved to the point that they no longer meet criteria for their particular disease. If the patient relapses and again presents with symptoms, hospice can be reinitiated. The same regulations would apply, and care would be started by the order of a physician.

10. Hospice care remains the same regardless of where the individual is in his prognosis.

FACT: To ensure the appropriate care at different times along the course of a patient's illness, care is divided into 4 levels as follows.

-   Routine level of care:

This is how hospice care is initiated. Patients are stable. Symptoms like pain or nausea and vomiting are adequately controlled. It usually is provided in the patient's home.

- General inpatient level of care (GIP):

This is a crisis-like level of care for short-term management of symptoms which are not well controlled. It is usually provided outside the home in an inpatient setting, at a medical facility like a hospital, or a skilled nursing facility.

- Continuous care:

This is also a crisis-like level of care for short term management of symptoms. The difference is this care is provided in the home. Registered nurses are scheduled to be in the home to assess pain and symptoms and assure the proper doses of medication are being prescribed for the patient. The nurse is in constant communication with the ordering physician.

- Respite care:

This is a level of temporary care provided in a nursing home, hospice inpatient facility, or other facility with which the hospice program has a contract. It is tied to the caregiver needs, not patient symptoms. It allows a family member or friend who's been the primary caregiver to take some time off. The number of days is limited. The hospice nurse would discuss this in detail with family members, as it is dictated by the insurance plan.

11. Complementary alternative therapies are not covered under the hospice program.

FACT: Hospice fully supports all modalities of treatment for pain and symptom management. They are not paid for by the hospice program. Things such as Reiki massage, healing touch, and acupuncture may be ordered by the physician. Hospice strives to work together with all practitioners to formulate the best plan of care and thereby have the best outcome.

12. Palliative care is like hospice care.

FACT: These two programs are not the same but do have similarities. The goal of both hospice and palliative care is to focus on symptom management and ensuring the patient's comfort. Palliative care permits the patient to continue to consult with specialists and possibly receive ongoing treatment. Hospice care does not. It is recommended that you speak with your attending physician to determine which program would be appropriate in your situation.

Bereavement in Hospice Care, Saying Goodbye

Bereavement is that period following the death of a person when the hospice team offers support to the surviving family members, to assist them in the grief process. Statistically speaking about 98% of hospices offer telephone calls, 98% send a letter or card at the time of the death and/or anniversary of the death. Many programs send brochures or other educational materials about grief. If it is determined that a person needs more one to one intervention, a grief counselor may be recommended from the community.

But what about the human side of this part of the hospice experience? The relationship between a hospice team and the hospice patients' families takes them from being virtual strangers to welcomed guests in their home. In some cases, they may even seem like family. That was certainly the experience for me with many of my patients.

My role as a hospice nurse has allowed me to provide a special, very personal type of care to everyone I have met along this journey. Information of a most confidential nature is often shared. This is held in high esteem. As we help prepare caregivers for the imminent death of their family member, we are also preparing to say goodbye. Many emotions come to the surface at this time, both from the standpoint of the family and caregiver and the hospice team member. I know each one has their own account of how each case unfolds, up to and at the time of the person's death. I will address how I was affected as a hospice nurse.

How did I view the emotional picture of saying goodbye to a patient? Each person was unique, and therefore the goodbye was unique as well. I can recall one patient who, along with his wife, would have a cup of tea waiting for me each time I visited. I planned his visit to be the last one of the day, so I would have some extra time to talk with them. I knew I only had a few of these visits left. They both knew this as well. It was his wife who brought up the idea of "goodbyes." She had become accustomed to my visits as much as her husband had and she voiced with sadness that she would miss my coming and what a positive experience hospice had been. This was a perfect opportunity for me to explain our bereavement program. I gave her the details about how we would keep in touch with her for about a year and a half through phone calls, newsletters, and a few visits. I could see that lifted her spirits. I too, would miss those hot cups of tea on those cold winter days. What is special way to be able to deliver care to these wonderful people.

Rituals are a very important part of death and grieving. I have learned a great deal about the customs of different religions, nationalities, and family preferences as they pertain to funeral planning and grief. One ritual common to most hospice programs is the yearly memory service that is held. For our program, it took place at a local church. It was usually held between Thanksgiving and Christmas, so the church was decorated for this glorious season. Hospice team members and volunteers each carried a flower to the altar, as the names of each patient we cared for the previous year were read. They were placed into a large vase, so that by the end of the ceremony, there was a beautiful bouquet. As I recall, we took it to the hospital and put in a place of honor in the oncology unit. Another year we had everyone bring teddy bears. They were placed on the altar steps during the ceremony. It was a great tribute to those who had been on our service and to their family members present at that time. These were then gathered and distributed to local pediatric units at the hospitals in our area.

Another year for the memory service, we ordered special Christmas ornaments. Each family attending would receive one. It gave everyone a sense of honoring those who had died. It helped those who were grieving to feel some sort of light as they placed the ornament on the tree. There were many positive comments about how their spirits were lifted. Coping with the first Christmas after the death of a loved one can be especially difficult. Our memory service was one way of allowing people, who were also experiencing these feelings, to come together.

After the program, we would gather for fellowship and Christmas cookies. Families who attended were not just the newly bereaved. Some had been coming for more than five years. I would always look for certain family members, whom I had been accustomed to seeing there. And they looked for me as well. We would reminisce and tell stories about their loved one as if they had just been here with us. It was a joyous reunion for us. It reaffirmed my belief in the hospice philosophy and renewed my enthusiasm for this type of care, which I so loved giving. This is the bond between a hospice nurse, her patients, and the family members that have so graciously invited her to walk with them on this special journey. It is indelible and never to be taken for granted. These people have a special place in my heart that sustains me as I continue my passion for end-of-life care. I know I am blessed.

Walking a Labyrinth: A Unique Way to Do Your Grief Work

As the bereavement follow-up ends, many hospice families verbalize feelings of a different type of loss as they say goodbye to the hospice team members. They have become accustomed to one person or another being in their home to give care and support to their loved ones and themselves. It is a different type of loss, a different type of grieving, and the staff often experience it as well. We encourage families to reach out to those who know them well, those other family members and friends that are most likely to be comfortable just sitting in silence. As I have addressed in the book, presence is a very powerful force. It can be a most unique gift when given with the right intention. It can bring a certain calm to an otherwise anxious situation. There are many ways people choose to deal with this part of their grief journeys. You will hear it referred to as grief work. It is exactly that because it takes emotional energy and a certain amount of intellectual planning. You must choose the tools you feel will work well for you. Meditation may be one of them. I offer you now, a variation of that ancient ritual.

There is a very private type of meditation known as labyrinth walking. It has its root in spiritual or meditative practice. Walking a labyrinth can mean anything you want. Some people walk labyrinths as a form of active meditation, while others do so as a spiritual pilgrimage. I offer it here to you who are grieving as part of the bereavement process. Labyrinths foster contemplativeness, active meditation, and even spiritual transformation. For our purposes, I would say it can be a path to healing.

Entering the serpentine path of a labyrinth, you walk slowly while quieting your mind and focusing on a spiritual question or prayer. You may be thinking of your loved one who has died and all the wonderful memories you hold so dear. You may be concentrating more on your own spirit. You may be asking for some type of healing. There is no one reason why people walk a labyrinth. There is no set time for how long it will take you. Each one is unique. Some may take only five minutes, while others may be significantly longer.

So how is this done? In simple terms, walking a labyrinth requires you to merely follow the pattern laid down with no puzzle to figure out. This lets your mind focus on your meditation or prayer. It symbolizes a journey to a predetermined destination. You simply enter the labyrinth at the beginning and walk the winding path until the end. It will mean different things to different people. The hope is that for our grieving families it may mean finding some answers, and most importantly, finding peace.

I have walked the labyrinth more than once. I would say it was a great awakening for me. It allowed me to process the many deaths I have attended in my hospice work. At times, I could feel their presence as if these special people were visiting me from the beyond. Some may call it the afterlife. When someone dies, there may be physical phenomenon which occur. You must be open to receiving them. I believe my labyrinth meditation helped me to do this.

In cases where my patients had animals, I would witness a definite change in their behavior. Some dogs would make a sound which I cannot even describe. It was somewhere between a crying out and a low, almost musical tone. The first time this happened, I was mesmerized. It almost seemed spiritual, so I sat there in silence with the animal. Somehow, I knew that their master's soul must be taking flight at that time. A chill came over me, then was quickly gone. There is a custom that calls for leaving a window open in the room where the person is dying. This is a very physical way of giving their soul a path to the beyond. In conversations with my patients and their families, I learned that most of them did believe in something like an afterlife. I felt that one of my final gifts to them was to be sure that they got to this place, wherever it may be. On one labyrinth journey, I came to a place in the path where I felt as if my feet were frozen. I went with the feeling. I remember experiencing a sweet scent in the air. I believe it was lavender. It suddenly occurred to me that one of my patients always had fresh lavender in a vase on her dresser. The calming power of lavender is well known. It certainly had that effect on me, as I remembered this sweet lady. The bond that was created between this flower, this person, and me has remained to this day. Whenever I pass a bush of lavender, she immediately comes to my mind. The clouds take a special formation, as if someone is smiling down at me. I believe it is her.

On one walk, I set the intention to help me understand the death of a small child I was caring for. I have to say this was a recurring struggle anytime a child came on to our hospice service. I consider myself a person of faith, but when confronted with a dying child, I feel this faith being tested. It is a most personal type of experience. Having two children of my own, I could not imagine how I would cope with such heartache. Part of my intention was trying to reconcile my anger with God. I wasn't certain that this could ever happen completely. I continued my walk. Taking each turn slowly and deliberately. I could feel my breathing becoming shallower. As I looked up, my eye caught a painting hanging on the wall. It may be one that you are familiar with. It is the scene where a guardian angel with beautiful wings is guarding a child crossing over a bridge which is in danger of breaking. I had seen this picture many times growing up. As I recall, it had a bedtime prayer under it. Was this my answer? Was this my way to peace? I have always believed that each of us has a guardian angel. Why had I not thought of this as I was struggling with the fact these little children were leaving their loved ones. I was lamenting the fact that they would now be alone. But they were not. Surely, their guardian angel attended to them in their last hours here on earth and most certainly guided them as they crossed over. My breathing returned to normal. A sense of peace came over me. There was a small window positioned in such a way that a glimmer of light shown on that picture. I dried my tears and continued with my meditation. My spirit was lighter. My soul was renewed, and my faith was restored.

I said a small prayer of thanks to God.

I consider every experience I have had as a hospice nurse a most special gift. Each death I have been present for renews my spirit. I am a runner in a great relay race. As my patient is dying, I can feel the baton being placed in my hand. That is the emotional strength I need to be ready to minister to my next patient. Walking the labyrinth has taught me the need to stop and rest. Just as the runner needs water to hydrate his body, this meditation hydrates my soul. How fortunate I am to be placed in such an honorable position. The family of my patient, Tuyet, impressed upon me how special this honor was. Little did I know that choosing nursing as my profession would lead me down such a glorious path. I say that with much humility. To those who ask if this is a depressing field, I give a hearty "No." For those called to hospice, it is a unique life lesson. It has humbled me and led me to appreciate everything God has given me. My sincere hope and prayer is that when my journey is ending, a hospice nurse will be guiding me. Perhaps God will recognize me as the person that helped so many others return to him. That will be my final prayer.

The following page illustrates what a simple labyrinth looks like. They come in many different forms and may be inside or outside. To locate a labyrinth, you can contact the Labyrinth Society which lists upcoming labyrinth seminars, group walks, and lectures throughout the US.

Example of a Labyrinth

TALKING WITH PROFESSIONALS

Coping and Caregiving: After They're Gone

All deaths are sudden, no matter how gradual the dying may be.

-Michael McDowell

When we suffer the loss of a person close to us, it affects every aspect of our life. Physically, emotionally, mentally, socially, their absence reverberates throughout our days. At times it can feel almost intolerable. Addressing this experience, and at times tolerating this distress is the beginning of coping with grief, loss, and bereavement.

As difficult as it is to talk about, we all will eventually experience the loss of someone we love. This experience is more profound when we are the caregiver to our loved one, and our loved one dies. This relationship of caregiver becomes a role in past tense. Just that fact alone is an aspect of the loss. You lose a role, a title that defined part of who you are.

How do we begin to address this task of coping, when so much of who we are and what we know has been forever changed? Let me start by saying that there is no one right way to cope with grief. There are similarities in our grief experiences, and culture can shape how we view and experience grief reactions, but as unique as we are as individuals, so may be our grief experience. There are many theories of grieving and stages of grief in the relevant literature (Kubler-Ross, 1997; Rando, 1993; Tucci & Doka, 2011) which can be helpful in identifying your experience. One thing that many of these lists have in common is that, although they are stages, they are not linear. Grief experts acknowledge that you can go through stages of grief in many configurations. It is not a step-by-step plan. Grief is more of a zig-zag roller coaster than a straight point to point ride. Since this is my mom's book, I will tell you a piece of life advice she taught me. "Feelings are never wrong. The actions you do in response to that feeling are what might be wrong, but never the feeling. Feelings are never wrong." She told me this as general advice, and I have applied in my personal and professional life. And it also applies to grieving. Feel all the emotions that come to you. Even the ones that are uncomfortable. You might feel guilty because once your loved one died, you felt the freedom to finally do what you wanted to do in life. Maybe you felt angry at your loved one for dying and leaving you. These are uncomfortable emotions. How can I even think these things when I love and miss them so much?! Psychologist Dr. Marsha Linehan describes these feelings as dialects: two opposite feelings that are true at the same time. If we examine our emotions, especially related to loss, we can see that there is a great deal of "Ands." You can feel relief AND overwhelming longing. You can feel anger AND great sadness. These emotions do not cancel each other out. They co-exist. Feeling all the emotions and allowing for the opposite ones to linger together is all a part of the grieving process. If we don't go through the emotions of grief, and acknowledge the loss, it stays unexpressed inside us and becomes heavy. This heaviness creates stress on our bodies and can make us sick. Expressing our grief is not only good for our psychological health, but our physical health as well.

Realize you may be triggered by seemingly mundane events of life. Places, smells, and sounds will have different meanings. You may have heightened senses or realizations to events. Having a breakdown in the Hallmark card aisle when seeing holiday cards or going food shopping and seeing your loved one's favorite cereal on the shelf, could bring you to tears. All of this is okay! Seemingly unimportant things will now be part of the mosaic of keeping your loved one's memory alive. My mom came home from work one day and told a story of a woman who had cared for her husband before he died. My mom noticed during this bereavement visit that there was a balloon in the room. The woman would not get rid of the balloon, because her husband had blown it up. It was the last evidence of his breath on this earth. If you are reading this and have cared for a loved one who has died, I am sure you have your own examples of seemingly ambiguous experiences that become part of your grief story. Allow yourself these moments and experiences.

It is said that grief is the price you pay for having loved someone so much. It is unexpressed love that can no longer be given to them. Grief has no timeline, and sometimes you will experience more grief and sorrow as time passes. I have had numerous clients in grief counseling who would explain that their grieving felt stronger, or their reactions were more intense, after the first year or two after a loss. This was confusing to them. Shouldn't I be adapting to this new life by now? Why does this almost feel worse?

The first year is about survival, completing tasks related to your loved one's death. Funerals, memorials, documents, paperwork, there is lots to do, and your emotions may be on autopilot just to get through it all. You may be in shock from the experience. It is not unusual for grief to feel bigger and more invasive after the first anniversary of the death of your loved one. Unfortunately, a great deal of support from others is usual given during the time right after your loved one has died. It is important to identify and surround yourself with people who will listen and support without judgment as the years progress.

Donna Schempp, LCSW, former Program Director at The Family Caregiver Alliance identifies specific caregiving experiences and tasks after a loved one dies. These include allowing yourself to experience grief, relief, sleep, self-forgiveness, and confusion as your role as caregiver ends and what to do next in your life. There is a re-entry into life as someone who is no longer a caregiver. It is okay to take some time to contemplate what to do next in your life. Take all the time you need. Addressing loneliness, finding new activities, taking care of physical and psychological needs, and slowly embracing life moving forward are all a part of this re-entry.

Just like the grieving process itself, your grief experience as a caregiver is uniquely yours. Ride the wave of grief and attend to your needs at your own pace. Take the time to grieve and be patient with yourself. Let yourself feel all the emotions that may come from your loss. It may help to write down your thoughts and experiences in a journal, in order to make sense of what you are feeling. Build or gather a support system of people you can go to who will listen to you without judgment or interjection. Create rituals, ceremonies, or something tangible to keep the connection to your loved one; to help you transition into a life without their physical presence, and to affirm your relationship and love for them. These rituals or ceremonies could be service oriented, for example, honoring your loved one by planting a tree, or flower or vegetable garden. Or maybe it's a ritual that revolves around their birthday or anniversary of their death, where family and friends can get together to share a meal or just spend time together. Whatever you feel is best for you. If you feel like you need more support, seek out counseling from a mental health professional. Many of us have specific training in end-of-life care and caregiving and would be honored to be a part of your grief journey, to support and guide your next steps.

"Your grief is your own. It may sneak up in moments that feel inconvenient. But the loss of someone you love was never something that was convenient. So, your grief won't be either. You will grieve. You will cry. You will break down. You will be a mess. But you don't owe anyone an apology for how you choose to grieve. Grief is messy. Grief is unkind. Grief comes bearing a heaviness you didn't know about before. But in that grief what you find is the kind of

people who will at least try to lighten the load of what it is you're carrying. No one can bring them back or make that pain go away. But on the other side of this coin that is grief is so much love for someone who left too soon."

-Kirsten Corley

Jenna L. Jebitsch, Psy.D.

References:

Ackerman, C. E. (2018, April 25). Three Grief Counseling Therapy Techniques & Interventions. *Positive Psychology.* https://positivepsychology.com/grief-counseling/

Boss, P. (1999). *Ambiguous loss: Learning to live with unresolved grief.* Harvard University Press.

Breen, L. J., Aoun, S. M., O'Connor, M. K., Johnson, A. D., & Howting, D. (2020). Effect of caregiving at end of life on grief, quality of life and general health: A prospective, longitudinal, comparative study. *Palliative Medicine, 34*(1), 145–154. https://doi.org/10.1177/0269216319880766

Burton, A. M., Haley, W. E., Small, B. J., Finley, M. A., Dillinger-Vasille, M., & Schonwetter, R. S. (2008). Predictors of well-being in bereaved former hospice caregivers: The role of caregiving stressors, appraisals, and social resources. *Palliative & Supportive Care, 6*(2), 149–158. https://doi.org/10.1017/s1478951508000230

Coelho, A., De Brito, M., Teixeira, P., Frade, P. R., Barros, L., & Barbosa, A. (2020). Family Caregivers' Anticipatory Grief: A Conceptual Framework for Understanding Its Multiple Challenges. *Qualitative Health Research, 30*(5), 693–703. https://doi.org/10.1177/1049732319873330

Doka, K. J. (2012). Caregiving & Grief. *Hospice Foundation of America.* https://hospicefoundation.org/Grief-(1)/Caregiving

Doka, K. J. (2016). *Grief is a journey: Finding your path through loss.* Simon and Schuster.

Grief Resources | Center for Research on End-of-Life Care. (n.d.). Weill Cornell Medicine. https://endoflife.weill.cornell.edu/grief-resources

Hospice Foundation of America - Helpful Grief Articles. (n.d.). Hospice Foundation of America. https://hospicefoundation.org/Grief-(1)/Journeys-with-Grief-Articles

Kübler-Ross, E. (1969). *On Death and Dying.* MacMillan.

Kübler-Ross, E., & Kessler, D. (2014). *On Grief and Grieving: Finding the Meaning of Grief Through the Five Stages of Loss.* Simon and Schuster.

Linehan, M. (2014). *DBT Skills Training Manual* (2nd ed.). Guilford Publications.

Prolonged Grief Resources | Center for Complicated Grief. (2021, May 14). The Center for Prolonged Grief.

https://prolongedgrief.columbia.edu/for-the-public/resources-2/

Rando, T. A. (1986). *Loss and Anticipatory Grief.* Free Press.

Rando, T. A. (1993). *Treatment of Complicated Mourning.* Research Press.

Resources | Ambiguous Loss. (n.d.). https://www.ambiguousloss.com/resources/

Sanders, C. M. (1999). *Grief: The Mourning After: Dealing with Adult Bereavement.* John Wiley & Sons Incorporated.

Schempp, D. (2013). When Caregiving Ends. *Family Caregiver Alliance.* https://www.caregiver.org/resource/when-caregiving-ends/?via=caregiver-resources,caring-for-yourself,grief-and-loss#

Schempp, D. (2014). The Emotional Side of Caregiving. *Family Caregiver Alliance.* https://www.caregiver.org/resource/emotional-side-caregiving/

Speaking Grief | Public Media Documentary and Awareness Initiative. (n.d.). https://speakinggrief.org/

Tucci, A. S., & Doka, K. J. (2011). *Beyond Kübler-Ross: New Perspectives on Death, Dying and Grief.*

Children and Grief

As we progress through life, we are faced with many changes and at times these changes can take the form of a loss. As adults we can name many losses that we have and the grief that we have felt due to these losses. Like adults, children also grieve when experiencing a loss. When we think of the losses in our lives, most of us think first of death, especially the death of a loved one. When we think about the experience of loss more broadly, we go through numerous losses throughout the lifespan: relationships end, we graduate from college or change jobs, experience illness, witness the aging of our parents and feel sadness over the loss of our own youth. Accordingly, there are many types of losses that children face throughout childhood: death of loved ones and pets, divorce, changing schools or grades from year to year, moving to a new house and neighborhood (therefore losing their old house and neighborhood), losing friends, and abandoning the comfort of childhood to enter the turbulence of adolescence. What we might think of as routine or mundane changes in life, to a child may be the first experience of living through the grief process. Just like adults may have to move or leave a job, children also feel a sense of loss when they move residences or leave a school to start a new one. Even the change of school grades

138

from year to year may bring a sense of loss to children -- having to say goodbye to their teachers and the environment to which they have become accustomed. And children must also face bigger losses—death of family members or friends, natural disasters that can change their lives completely, loss of innocence and sense of safety due to preparing for potential school shootings, having a family member deployed by the military or hard economic times that force the family to change its lifestyle completely.

Grief Reactions

When we experience a loss in our lives, we also experience grief. According to Therese Rando, a grief expert, grief can be defined as the process of psychological, social, and somatic or bodily reactions to the perception of a loss, which is a natural and expected reaction to have when we have had an attachment to someone or something. Notice in the definition is the word *perception:* What one person may see as a loss, another may not. And this difference applies to children as well. Everyone experiences grief and loss differently and therefore expresses it differently, including what they see as a loss.

Not all children will react the same way or see an experience similar to their peers. Culture may also play a part in how children see loss and their grief response. However, when children do identify loss, there are similarities in the way children express grief, especially when looking at different developmental stages. Children under age three may express feelings of loss by increasing their dependence on their caretakers or not being as social as usual; children who are ages three to five may have temper tantrums or increase their activity. For school-aged children and adolescents, there may be noticeable changes in school performance and somatic complaints or symptoms of depression or anxiety such as fatigue, tearfulness, and loss of appetite. Overall, adults should be mindful of any changes in a child's behavior after experiencing a loss and help children express feelings of grief.

In terms of hospice care and preparing for a loved one's death, hospice team can be a valuable asset and support to a family facing such an unbearable task of saying goodbye to their loved one. Preparing for the death of a loved one and managing your own emotions and experiences can be overwhelming. The hospice team, especially the hospice social worker, can provide comfort and age-appropriate resources to the children and adolescents in the family, so everyone's needs are met during a time when the adults in the family are navigating their own grief journey.

What you can do to help
Children and adolescents can learn from adults in their life how to grieve in healthy, appropriate ways. To help children learn about grief and loss, adults can be role models:
- Grieve your own losses so they can learn from you.
- Teach about the feelings associated with grief such as sadness, guilt, or anger. Discuss why you are sad.

- Ask about feelings and thoughts and observe the children's actions and behaviors. Do not ignore their feelings or dismiss how they feel.
- Normalize feelings of grief; communicate to them that it is okay to feel the way they do. For example, anger can be scary to feel towards a loved one who has died, or towards a parent during a divorce. Help them understand why they are having these feelings and that it is a normal part of grieving.

Interventions for Children

When we involve children and adolescents in rituals of death and dying, consideration must be given to their age, developmental, and intellectual level in order to assess their level of understanding. In addition, you should discuss their willingness to participate in these rituals or events, including their presence at the time of their loved one's death, attendance at the funeral, memorial, or other rituals or events that may be planned. Prepare the child or adolescent for what they are going to see or experience. Sometimes adults worry that they will make the child or adolescent afraid of the experience by telling them this information; however, providing information diffuses anxiety and can provide a level of preparedness and normalization, so they know what to expect. It helps them realize that grief reactions are ok and normal.

Again, information should be given in a way that takes the child or adolescent's age and understanding into consideration. Children and adolescents should never be forced to participate in rituals or events related to the death of a loved one. If they express hesitation, provide information about these rituals and events to educate them; however, the decision should be up to them. Losing a loved one is an event that we do not have control over, so therefore we need to have control over how we grieve- and children and adolescents should have control over this as well.

Ritualizing the loss is an important part of helping children grieve appropriately. We have rituals for death and dying, but including other losses that children and adolescents may experience will also help them express their grief. Rituals help children express themselves in their own way and help guide them toward healing. They move forward using healthy coping and self-expression.

Other rituals of grieving and loss for children and adolescents may include:

- Planting flowers or trees to symbolize a loved one or pet or the loss of a friendship.
- Have a funeral or a memorial service for a family pet.
- Discuss favorite memories of their classmates or teachers at the end of a school year.
- Have them "say goodbye" to their house when they move and discuss the favorite memories they have had there; take pictures or make a video of the house for them to watch later to help keep the memories alive.
- Use expressive arts—painting, coloring, music, poetry, or journaling—to help express their feelings.
- Make a scrapbook of a loved one using photographs and drawings.

- With the help of an adult, light a candle symbolizing a loss and talk about it.
- If they need additional help, have the child attend an age-appropriate support group or hospice bereavement group to help them deal with the loss of a loved one, or seek additional grief counseling services from a licensed mental health professional.

Children are faced with many different types of loss during childhood. As adults, we want to shield them from any unpleasant events and maintain their innocence. But, as part of the human family, they experience loss and grief like all of us. We have the ability to teach and model how we adapt to changes and losses in order for them to learn appropriate coping skills. Listening to children and giving the opportunity for children to talk about their experiences with loss and grief can help them resolve the negative aspects of grief in their lives and adjust well to any challenges they may face in the future.

Jenna L. Jebitsch, Psy.D.

References:

Davidson, J. (2002). *Grief Skills for Life: A Personal Journal for Adolescents about Loss*. Walton, KY: Renew Center for Personal Recovery, Inc.

Fry, V. L. (1995). *A Part of Me Died, Too: Stories of Creative Survival Among Bereaved Children and Adolescents*. New York: Penguin Group USA, Inc.

Heegaard, M. (1988). *When Someone Very Special Dies: Children Can Learn to Cope with Grief.* Minneapolis: Woodland Press.

Jebitsch, J. L. (2009). Children and the experience of loss: How to help children grieve. *Healing,* *14*(1), 12-13.

Keckler, B. & Davis, D. (2005). *From Here to There.* Richardson, TX: Blue Sky Media Group.

Papalia, D. E. (2007). *Human Development (10th Ed.).* Boston: McGraw-Hill.

Rando, T. (1993). *Treatment of Complicated Mourning.* Champaign, IL: Research Press.

ABOUT THE AUTHOR

Linda J. Mancinelli is a Hospice and Palliative Care nurse. She has devoted more than 30 years to the care of terminally ill patients and their families. She believes educating the public on end-of-life care is a much-needed subject. To that end, she has spoken to civic organizations, service clubs and local community colleges about hospice care. Her philosophy maintains that every dying person is entitled to die with dignity and the best pain and symptom management possible. Likewise, that their families feel supported and knowledgeable in the care of their loved ones, as they take that final journey to the dying process.

ABOUT THE CONTRIBUTORS

Jenna L. Jebitsch, Psy.D. is a licensed psychologist and co-owner of Generation of Change, a counseling and mental health consulting practice in Allentown, PA. Dr. Jebitsch has over 20 years of experience as a mental health professional and has specialized training in providing grief counseling services to those who are experiencing grief and loss.

Brian P. Yount is an artist, illustrator, and freelance web designer. He is currently the marketing director for a web media company in Allentown, PA